Little Miss Somebody

Christy Lynn Abram

Humble Bee Publishing
TACOMA, WASHINGTON

Little Miss Somebody/ Christy Lynn Abram. – 1st ed.
ISBN:978-0-692-38622-4

To my Sister
Sherranda
You are a bright light.
Thank you for that!

For all those who are still struggling with finding their peace. I love you. We love you. We're in this together.

"You own everything that happened to you. Tell your stories. If people wanted you to write warmly about them, they should have behaved better."
— Anne Lamott, Bird by Bird

This book contains subject matter about sexual assault and/or violence which may be triggering to survivors.

ST. LOUIS, MISSOURI 1993

One

"HEY, WHITE GIRL!" I heard a voice as I passed by. I turned to find the lead G-G (Ghetto Girl), Sophia, standing with her hand on her hip.

I took a deep breath and answered, "Yeah?"

"I heard you've been talking to my boyfriend, Arthur."

"Who?"

"You know who I'm talking about. Don't play stupid!"

"I don't know what you're talking about." I shook my head in puzzlement.

"Arthur said you stalked him at Saint's until he gave you his number, even though he told you he had a girlfriend."

I wanted to tell Sophia that it was the other way around, but I knew it would only infuriate her.

"Sorry, I think you have the wrong person."

"No, I don't. He described you. The dirty girl from Washington who thinks she's white." Sophia's crew burst into laughter as she stood there with her arms crossed, staring me up and down. I was pissed, but instead of arguing back, I muttered, "Whatever," and walked off.

"That's alright. You ain't going to be saying 'whatever' when I kick your ass after school!"

I knew I shouldn't have told Arthur where I went to school. It wasn't like we went out or anything. He was just a boy I met at Saint's a couple of weeks ago. All we did was talk on the phone. Besides, I liked someone else—an older boy named André.

Oh, man, what have I gotten myself into? I thought.

The G-Gs were always giving me problems for no reason. I think they were mad because the boys at school liked me; they were always calling me "cutie" and "fine." The G-Gs constantly called me names like "dirty white girl" because I spoke "proper," or "white", as they called it. They also hated the fact that I was light-skinned with what black people call "good hair."

They were the reason I hated King Middle School. It was rough and harsh—a lot different than my school in Washington State. At that moment, I really missed Washington. I had a lot of friends there and never had to worry about girls trying to fight me over stupid stuff. Honestly, I was tired of fighting.

Now, I'd had my share of rumbles, but the G-Gs were professionals. If they knew they couldn't beat someone, they would jump them. I was scared, but I wasn't going to stand there and let them punk me. My plan was to hit as many of them as possible and try to get away. I wasn't sure if it would work, but it was worth a try.

Me and my cousin, Meechie, both went to King Middle School. Although we were in the same grade, we didn't have any classes together. I looked down the hall where her class was to see if I could find her. My white canvas shoes squeaked as I ambled down the massive hallway. I anxiously surveyed every slim, brown-skinned girl with an orange backpack, but she was nowhere in sight. I hoped and prayed that Meechie would come to my rescue if she saw me getting beat down by those crazy-ass girls.

The day flew by. Before I knew it, the last bell rang and school was over. Fearing the worst, I reached down to make sure my shoes were tied tightly, and then removed my earrings so they couldn't be ripped off my ears.

I trudged into the hall and out the front door. Surprisingly, the G-Gs weren't there. My bus was parked outside the door so I figured if I hurried, I could get on the bus before the G-Gs saw me. I walked down the stairs, but before I reached the sidewalk I heard, "There she goes!" I quickly turned around to find Sophia and seven girls standing behind me. I almost peed my pants.

"Thought you could get away, huh? Did you think I was going to let you get away with messing with my boyfriend?"

"Sophia, what is your problem? Why are you always messing with me?"

"I don't like you. You're a bum who thinks she's

cute. Look at you, ketchup stains all on your pants. Dang, you don't have a washing machine?"

The G-G crew laughed and heckled me while Sophia made me the highlight of the day. What Sophia didn't know was I didn't have a washing machine and Mama hadn't been home in days. Tears filled my eyes, but instead of crying, I snapped back.

"You're just mad because your boyfriend thinks I'm prettier than you."

The crowd exploded, "Oooooooo!" My comment stung Sophia, but the sadness in her face was quickly replaced by rage.

"Who do you think you're talking to?" Sophia pushed me hard in the middle of my chest, causing me to stumble backwards and trip over a crack in the cement. "Yeah, you ain't got all that mouth now, do you?"

The crowd burst into laughter. Others yelled, encouraging Sophia to hit me. "Get her, Sophia!"

I quickly jumped to my feet and searched for options. I looked at the bus parked to my right and tried to imagine a way to run for it. I could see Meechie looking out the window, trying to figure out what the commotion was. As the G-Gs balled up their fists and circled me, I thought, *This is it. They're going to beat me up! I guess I'll have to go out fighting.* I readied my body for the first blow.

Just then, Meechie ran off the bus and stood beside me. She had her fists balled up, ready to fight. "Y'all ain't about to jump my cousin!"

I was relieved, but there were still eight of them

against the two of us. Luckily, the school security guard saw the crowd gathering and ordered everyone to disperse.

"Y'all better get out of here before I call 5-0 on y'all little asses," the round security guard demanded.

Sophia snickered, "Looks like you got saved today, white girl. Next time, you won't be that lucky."

"I said, get out of here!" the security guard waved his arms and repeated. Then he drew his attention to me and Meechie. "Girls, don't worry about them. Go ahead and get on your bus." We reluctantly turned our backs to the G-Gs and began walking towards the bus.

"What was that all about?" Meechie asked me.

"Don't know. Something about Arthur telling Sophia I was stalking him."

"I told you not to give that boy our number. He's always amping Sophia up, knowing she likes to fight."

We got on the bus. Adrenaline surged through my veins, causing my heart to beat wildly. I almost got pummeled by the G-Gs. I sat in silence the whole way home.

Well, at least my pants are dry. Glad today is the last day of school. I thought.

I looked forward to seeing Mama. *Maybe she'll give me some money to get something to eat and wash my clothes.* My thoughts wandered until I felt the bus come to a stop.

"Come on! We're here!" Meechie tugged at my arm. "You never pay attention."

Meechie was right, I didn't pay attention. My mind was always wondering about this or that. Often, I worried about what I was going to eat that day or how

I would get the bare necessities to take care of myself. Meechie was always on point. She was a "straight A" student who possessed an overwhelming amount of spunk. Meechie, her sister Erin, their mama TeeTee and I all lived together at Grandma's. Aunt TeeTee was on drugs and was usually gone, but somehow she managed to be home more than Mama.

Every month, Meechie received a Social Security check because someone put something in her daddy's drink at a bar and he went crazy. It was the only thing her father ever did for her. Her SSI check allowed her to take care of herself. That is, if TeeTee or Uncle Lee didn't steal her money. Meechie usually had to sleep with her money in her bra or give it to Grandma for safekeeping.

TeeTee was nice to me sometimes, but she was always fussing. She would say, "You being here is taking away from my kids."

Every time I asked to cook something or went in the refrigerator, she would yell, "Where's your mama? Ain't nobody got money to be taking care of you!" I tried not to take it personally, but it hurt my feelings. I just figured it was the drugs talking and ignored her the best way I could. Other times, I felt she only picked on me because she and Mama didn't get along.

Mama told me Aunt TeeTee got away with murder when they were younger. She said, "Grandma would let her stay out late at night, but I had to be in at a decent hour."

Mama thought TeeTee was in competition with her; that's why TeeTee got pregnant at 15, because Mama was five months pregnant with me. Ever since TeeTee got on drugs, their relationship worsened. They argue and roll their eyes at each other when the other is talking. Mama called TeeTee a crackhead and got mad at Grandma, saying she enabled her. Personally, I felt Mama didn't have any room to judge anyone. She was an alcoholic, who was never home for me. Alcohol wasn't cocaine, but it kept her away just as much as TeeTee, if not more.

We walked across North Pointe Boulevard and up the street to the house. Meechie made fun of me, saying, "You almost got beat up today. What would you have done if I wasn't on the bus?"

"They probably would've beat me up, but I would've fought as hard as I could," I answered.

"Girl, please. Ain't no probably about it. They would've beat your tail up."

We laughed as we approached the house. Uncle Lee was sitting on the front porch, smoking a cigarette and giving us the evil eye.

"What y'all laughing at?"

"Nothing! You're always in somebody's business," said Meechie, rolling her eyes.

"You better watch your mouth, little girl, before I punch you in it!"

"Whatever! With your ole' ugly self," she mumbled as she opened the metal screen door.

Meechie and Uncle Lee didn't get along. Uncle Lee was notorious for stealing everyone's money and food. He was short, skinny and missing his two front teeth. When he was younger, everyone called him "Wheels" because he liked to roller skate. Everything changed when he got addicted to crack. Now, Uncle Lee spends his time washing cars for money and hiding in the basement until he gets his next fix.

I giggled under my breath and hurried to pass Uncle Lee before he started on me, but it was too late.

"What are you laughing at, dirty little girl? That's why you got ketchup on your pants."

"So what! That's why you don't have any front teeth!" I said, sticking out my tongue.

Meechie fell over in laughter. "That was a good one!"

I was proud. Uncle Lee was always making fun of me. I had finally gotten payback. I wanted to say more, but he was infamous for trying to fight me and my cousins, and I'd had enough drama for one day.

One time, he and Meechie got into a fight and she swung so hard her arm popped out of its socket. She told me it hurt badly and she had to go to the hospital to get her shoulder bone "snapped" back in. Since then, every time she got into a fight, one or both of her arms would dislocate. It felt good to know Meechie would risk dislocating her arm to protect me. I loved Meechie. She always came through, no matter what.

My family was no stranger to violence. They loved to fight. They fought each other, the neighborhood kids and anyone else who messed with one of us. Grandma told me when Mama and Aunt TeeTee were younger, in the '70s, before we were born, they would always get into fights with girls in the neighborhood. Mama, TeeTee and my Grandma's sisters Sandy and Eunice, would meet their rivals on the train tracks at the top of the street, with bats and chains, and battle it out. Aunt

TeeTee had even been shot before. They were tough. No wonder the rest of us had heart. I guess we learned from the best.

There were mostly girls in our family, but we carried on like boys. They were always bragging about who they beat up or they would be threatening to "kick somebody's ass." If one of us got into a fight and came home crying, we were told not to come home until we beat them. Aunt TeeTee, would say, "You ain't no punk. You better go find them and beat their ass."

I didn't understand why fighting was so important. In Tacoma, I could hang out and have fun with my friends, without the drama of arguing and fighting. St. Louis was different. It seemed everyone had something to prove. I didn't find fighting fun; I wanted to relax and laugh. Besides, I had other things on my mind.

CHAPTER

Two

"MA-MA!" MEECHIE CALLED as she dropped her bag on the living room floor.

"She's not here," Uncle Lee yelled from the front porch.

"What time is it? Where's Erin?"

I listened to Meechie talk to herself while I relaxed on the couch. Meechie was busy looking in the fridge for something to eat.

"There's never anything here to eat!" she announced.

I chuckled under my breath in agreement. "I know."

"My mama ain't gone grocery shopping this month. I think she sold the food stamps again. That's probably why we ain't seen her in a couple of days. I hate when she does that."

Aunt TeeTee being on crack was embarrassing to

Meechie. She tried to hide her hurt under her anger, but I knew it upset her to see TeeTee high.

Grandma told me Aunt TeeTee, whose real name was Lauren, started smoking crack when Uncle Lorenz died in a car accident a few years back. She said TeeTee and Lorenz were tight and she just couldn't get over his death.

I didn't remember much about Uncle Lorenz, but Mama told me when I was a baby he would take me out with him so he could pick up women. He would lie and tell them my mom left him to take care of me alone. Mama said he would come home with a pocket full of phone numbers, and I would have ice cream all over my face.

Meechie went to her secret spot to count her money then came back with a crisp $20 bill in her hand.

"I'm about to order some Chinese food from Chang's. You want to walk with me?"

"Yeah, I'll go."

Meechie picked up the phone to order her meal. I sat there hoping she would order me something, too. I was embarrassed to ask, so I sat in silence listening to my stomach growl. I knew Meechie would share with me, but I felt bad because she had to make sure Erin ate, too.

Instead, I went to the kitchen and looked through the cabinets. I was lucky to find a pack of chicken-flavored instant noodles hidden behind some empty boxes. I felt like I had won the lottery. I hid the noodles behind the toaster and waited for Meechie by the door.

"Are you ready?"

"Yep."

"Come on. Let's hurry up and get back before Erin gets home."

Grandma's street was quiet; however, a couple of blocks over it was a completely different story. Drug dealers and gang members were common characters in Grandma's neighborhood. We had to pass that block to get to Chang's, which was only a couple of blocks away on West Florissant. Grandma always told us to walk together.

Mr. Chang had been a staple in Grandma's neighborhood for years. He served up the best fried rice or "Chinamen" in the Northside neighborhood of St. Louis. "Chinamen" is what everyone in my family called the Chinese restaurant. I thought it was mildly derogatory, but everyone said it, so I felt it was okay. Although Chang's restaurant was a hole in the wall with three tables and a bench, everyone went to Chang's. Even the most unsavory characters: bums, gang members and local dope boys all looking to gain something. The dope boys were always flashing their sparkly gold teeth and harassing girls as they walked in.

"Hey, girl, let me holler at you for a minute."

Chang had a habit of telling everyone their order would be ready in 15 minutes, but we always had to wait when we got there.

Meechie and I didn't talk much on our way to Chang's. I mostly listened to the symphony happening in my belly and wished my pants had more than a buffet of ketchup on them.

"Chang, is my order ready?" Meechie asked, tossing her money on the counter.

"Five minutes!" Chang said, peeking out of the little

window on the counter.

"Hurry up. I'm hungry."

Sitting in Chang's for those five minutes tripled my hunger. I was relieved to hear Chang call Meechie's order. "Special fried rice with egg foo young gravy."

Meechie grabbed her food and we headed back to the house. The aroma of her fried rice forced me to think about the pack of instant noodles that awaited me.

Between my thoughts, I could hear Meechie rambling on about her plan to see her boyfriend, Eric, and go to Saints that weekend.

Saints was a skating rink in the Olivette where everyone hung out on Saturday nights. It was like a club for teenagers. It even had a party room, equipped with flashing lights and a D.J. All of the players and dealers were always in attendance, along with the girls who aspired to be their girl-friends.

"Who are you going with?" I asked.

"I don't know. Why? You want to go?"

"Yeah, but I don't have any money."

"Your mama ain't been home yet?"

"No, I haven't seen her in days. Maybe she'll come home this weekend."

"Where she be going anyway?"

"I don't know."

Meechie paused. "Do you think she's smoking crack?"

"Nah, I don't think so. I've never seen her high, just drunk."

It wasn't farfetched that Mama would be smoking crack. There were a lot of crackheads in our neighborhood. My stomach began to hurt more at the thought of Mama smoking a crack pipe in an alley or abandoned building. Although, that would've explained why she was never home.

Meechie and I made it back safely to the house. Meechie sat at the table to prepare her rice with the condiments Chang left in her brown paper bag. I headed for the kitchen to make my noodles. I grabbed a pot from under the counter, filled it with water and turned on the stove.

When the water boiled and it was time to add the noodles, I couldn't find them. They weren't in the spot where I hid them. I looked all over the counter and on the floor. They were no place in sight. I knew only one person could have taken them—Uncle Lee.

"Uncle Lee!" I yelled down the stairs.

"What!"

"Did you eat my noodles?"

"Yep, shouldn't have left them. They're mine now!"

My heart sank with disappointment. I didn't get a chance to eat because I skipped lunch to dodge the G-Gs. I sat at the table, fuming, with tears in my eyes.

"What's wrong with you?" Meechie asked, stirring her rice.

"Lee ate my noodles."

"You left them out? That was stupid."

"No, I hid them behind the toaster."

"Girl, he knows that hiding place. Nowadays you have to take your food with you or hide it somewhere you know he won't find it.

Get a bowl."

I sprung out of my seat as if it was Christmas morning. Meechie gave me half of her rice. I ate it quickly. I even licked the bowl when she wasn't looking.

Erin came in a little while later, full of energy and attitude.

"What you eating, Meechie?"

"I went to Chang's and got some rice."

"Ooooh, I want some," Erin said, looking in Meechie's rice box.

"It's gone."

"Why didn't you save me some?"

"Little girl, you better leave me alone. Ask Grandma to buy you some when she gets home."

Erin was a few years younger than Meechie. Just like me and my sister Sissy, her and Meechie didn't have the same daddy, but that didn't matter. They were thick as thieves. She was a smart-mouthed little somebody who could hold her own. She was always rolling her neck, causing the multi-colored balls in her hair to swing.

Meechie and Erin continued to argue back and forth, until Erin retreated to their room to change her clothes. I sat at the table, looking out the window until I grew tired of the noise and decided to sit on the front porch.

I watched the little kids return from school wearing their blue-and-white uniforms and listened to the random basses from cars passing by on the street above. Grandma's street was a one-way. Most of the traffic on the street was from neighbors or visitors.

All the homes on the block were brick, with wood shutters and covered porches. I loved the look of the neighborhood—it gave the appearance that hard-working, middle-class people lived there. Since most of the homes on the street were occupied by older people, the lawns were always neat and the street tidy. It wasn't unusual to see people sitting on their front porches, drinking cool drinks and enjoying the shade. Since Grandma had been living in the Northside for over twenty years, she knew all the neighborhood kids and their mothers. They called her Mrs. Rose.

Most of the people who lived on the Northside had been there for many years. If they didn't know your name, they damn sure knew your mama's or grandparents' names. It wasn't odd to be reprimanded by the matriarchs of the neighborhood. If one of them saw you doing something, they would make sure you got in trouble for whatever you did.

Grandma told me black people weren't always welcomed in her neighborhood. She said, "When black folks started moving into the city, they did their best to run us out. They threatened us, destroyed our property and worse, but we fought through it and stayed."

I couldn't imagine white people staying in Grandma's neighborhood; I never saw any. I did, however, understand the unpleasantness of white people in St. Louis.

Each time I went with Grandma to the buffet at the Clocktower Plaza, in St. Louis County, the white people always gave us mean looks. It felt as though they didn't want us there. I would ask Grandma why they were looking at us that way and she would tell me not to pay them any mind. She also reminded me that Missouri was the last state to abolish slavery and some white people felt we didn't deserve to be free.

Seeing how badly black people were treated intensified my craving for Washington. The truth was I hadn't experienced racism there. The white people I encountered there were nice and helpful. I felt welcomed there; not so much in St. Louis.

I sat and thought about how much I missed my friends and family in Washington. I wished I could go back there. Before we left, I asked Donny, my step-dad, if I could stay and he told me no. Something about my dad not letting him adopt me. I didn't understand what the big deal was. It wasn't like my dad ever called or came to see me.

In fact, we'd been in St. Louis for more than a year and he never came by. Mama said he lived 30 minutes over the bridge in Alton, Illinois, but when I asked for his number, she always changed the subject. At this point, I'd only seen him once—the summer I came to visit Grandma when I was 11. He told me he was going to come and get me the next day, so we could spend time together. I waited on the front porch all day, but he never came. I was hurt and disappointed. Mama voiced her opinion by telling me, "I told you his no-good ass wasn't coming."

I didn't know too much about my dad, other than the stories I heard from Grandma. She told me he was an attractive guy, with a big Afro and thick glasses, who drove a yellow Pinto. Grandma told me Mama was in love with him, but he broke her heart. I don't think she ever recovered. She referred to him as a piece-of-shit playboy who screwed every chick in town.

I could tell Mama hated him, yet she often reminded me of how much I looked like him. Maybe that's why she was never home—she hated me too. She sure treated me like she did. Every time I tried to talk to Mama, she ignored me. If I pushed too hard for attention, she would yell and curse, "Get your worrisome ass out of my face!"

Other times, she would throw things at me or beat me with brooms, belts or her fist. My fear of her caused me to be afraid to ask her anything. She was so mean and hateful towards me, but I loved her unconditionally. Mama was all I had in St. Louis. Everything I'd grown to know for the last ten years was in Washington. Every day, I questioned why she ripped me from my friends and family. I wondered if bringing me to St. Louis was part of her plan to get rid of me.

On the days when my pain became unbearable, I wrote to God in my journal. Donny always encouraged me and Sissy to read and write. We played Scrabble a lot, too. He told me, "Education is important. If you're smart, you'll go far in life." I looked up to Donny, so it was easy to follow his directions. Writing to God kind of reminded me of me, Donny and Sissy praying together before bed. It made me feel safe. I felt God was the only person who could understand what I was feeling and eventually fix Mama.

I wanted her to be happy, but I didn't know how to help her. She always looked so sad and occupied; maybe that's why she drank and partied as much as she did. I felt sorry for looking like the man who hurt her so deeply. My sympathy forced me to feel obligated to right his wrongs. In some way, I felt I deserved to suffer if it meant that one day I would have the opportunity to feel loved by Mama. *I'll do my best to make Mama happy. Then she'll love…I hope.*

CHAPTER Three

THE DAY ENDED and, as usual, there was still no sign of Mama. It seemed each week she stayed gone for longer periods. Although I had gotten used to her disappearing acts, this time she was gone for a week. I assumed she was hanging out with her newest boyfriend.

I thought, *She's probably living it up while I'm here with no clean clothes or food.*

Instead of obsessing about Mama and her whereabouts, I decided to pass the time by calling André, the boy I met at Saints the week before. I met André in the party room at the Saints Roller Rink. He and his friends were posed up on the wall, checking out the females who walked by. I saw him from across the room. I figured if I walked past and swished my butt a little, I would get his attention. I waited until a song I liked came on before I executed my plan. I wanted to make sure my bounce looked authentic.

On cue, I heard the words to my favorite song, *Sally Walk* by Stetsasonic. I grabbed Meechie's hand. "Come on. Let's walk around."

I made sure, when we walked past him, that I did the Sally Walk hard, and it worked. He followed me and asked for my name and gave me his number. André looked older than me. He had no idea I was 14. I lied and told him I was 16 after he said he was 17. I think he knew I was lying, but he gave me his number anyway.

André was fine. He was tall and brown-skinned, with perfect white teeth. He rocked a low-cut haircut with waves all over. He also dressed fly. That night, he wore Guess jeans, a paisley shirt and a pair of fresh white Reeboks. He looked like he had money.

In my neighborhood, the girls who dated dope dealers got to wear nice jewelry, get their hair done and sport the latest fashions. I figured the only way I was going to keep money in my pocket and look fly was to become a dope boy's chick. I thought André could save me from struggling at Grandma's house and feeling lonely. I was desperate, so I was willing to lay on my charm to get what I wanted.

I called the number he gave me. It was a beeper. I knew only important guys had beepers and car phones. In a way, André reminded me of my Uncle Teddy. He always dressed nice and drove nice cars, not to mention his beeper was always going off. I'm pretty sure he sold drugs, too. Uncle Teddy wasn't around much, but I looked up to him. He was always nice to me.

Last summer, Teddy asked me to ride with him to

meet his friends a few blocks over on Mimika Avenue. When I got in the car, he put an oversized, brown MGM purse in my lap and told me to hold it. When we made it to our destination, he opened the bag and there were four white balls inside, wrapped in plastic. Uncle Teddy got out of the car and handed the bag to two guys who looked alike. In exchange, they gave him a brown paper bag.

When Teddy got back in the car he told me to NEVER tell anyone, then peeled a crisp $50 bill from a huge wad of cash and gave it to me.

I put André's number in and waited for the phone to ring. Shortly after, he called back. "Somebody beep me?" His voice was deep, yet there was an innocence to it.

"Yeah, this is Nikki!"

"Nikki, who?" he asked.

"You know, the girl you met at Saints last week?"

"Oh, the cute girl with the pretty eyes? What's up, cutie?"

"Yes," I replied.

"I've been waiting for you to call me. What are you doing this weekend?"

"Nothing much. Waiting for my Mama to get home."

"You're not going to Saints this weekend?"

"I don't know. It depends if I can get a ride."

"Well, let me know. If not, you can come over to the spot."

"Where's the spot?"

"On the Northside by the Sears building. Just call me

when you're coming and I'll tell you how to get there."

"Okay, I'll let you know."

"Alright, cutie. Talk to you later."

The smile on my face was so big, I felt the corners of my mouth cracking. An older boy with money showed an interest in me and asked me to come over. Now, all I needed was for Mama to come home so I could wash my clothes. I can't go see André with ketchup stains and dirt smudges on my clothes. I had to give him the impression that I was fly; that way he would want me to be his girl.

For the next fifteen minutes, I practiced being sexy in the bathroom mirror. I stuck out my chest and poked out my butt to see how appealing it was. At 14, my boobs weren't that big. I stuck tissue paper in my bra to make them look big and round. I ran from the bathroom, hoping to find Meechie in the dining room to show her my newest additions, but was surprised to discover Grandma and Granddaddy sitting at the kitchen table.

Embarrassed, I crossed my arms, hoping Grandma didn't notice the uneven bulges protruding from my dingy white shirt.

"Hi, Grandma! Where've you been?" I asked, leaning against the door frame.

"Me and your Granddaddy have been out all day running around. We just came from that fish place down the street, getting something to eat."

The aroma of catfish permeated all through the house, filling each room with its unmistakable aroma.

"Did you eat?" she asked me.

"No. Not really. Uncle Lee ate the last pack of

noodles. Meechie gave me some of her rice, though."

"Has your Mama made it home yet?"

"No."

"Do you want some of this fish?"

"Yes."

"Go get a plate."

I scampered to the kitchen cabinet to get a plate. Before coming back, I reached under my shirt to retrieve my fake boobs and threw them in the trash can, then hurried back for my serving of Grandma's stinky, delicious fish. Just as I reached for a piece, I heard my Granddaddy say, "What are you doing?!?"

"Grandma said I could have a piece of fish."

"No you can't! Where's your Mama? Tell her to get you some fish."

Granddaddy was always fussing, usually about nothing. I think he just liked the sound of his voice, which was interesting because most times I had no idea what he was saying. Granddaddy, an illiterate country man, grew up in Mississippi, but had been living in St. Louis for a long time. I guess he never lost his accent.

He worked long hours at a factory and hustled DVDs and whatever else he could get his hands on in his free time. We didn't see him much, but when he was home everyone knew it. He would be sitting at the kitchen table watching wrestling or eating with his dentures on the table beside him. He and Grandma met when Lee was a baby. He was mean and grouchy, but he loved Grandma and the rest of us too.

"Oh, be quiet," my Grandma fired back. "She can have some!"

"Go on 'head. That's a damn shame! Your Mama ain't been here in days. She's got to know you're hungry."

"Henry, be quiet. She don't need to hear that."

"It's the truth. Her mama been leaving that child here for us to take care of since she been back in St. Louis. Look at her, all dirty and stuff. Somebody needs to call the people on her."

"Ain't nobody calling the people on anybody. Why put them white people in our business?" Grandma turned to me, "Baby, get your piece of fish. Don't mind your granddaddy."

The truth hurt, but I took his banter because I was hungry.

"Hurry up and eat it before the rest of them come begging," Granddaddy grumbled.

Grateful for a decent meal, I sat and talked to Grandma for a while before she took a nap and got ready for work. She worked nights as a nurse at an assisted living center. In the day, she usually slept in, but sometimes I could catch her sitting at the kitchen table drinking coffee.

Me and Grandma were close. I think I was her favorite; after all, I was her first grandchild. Her and I talked a lot about my dream of becoming a fashion designer. I would tell her that I was going to be rich one day and buy her a big house. She would giggle and say, "I know you will, baby."

Although I didn't look like much, I loved to read Vogue magazine and sketch models wearing my eclectically styled clothes. She told me she believed I could be whoever I wanted to be. Mama, on the other hand, told me I wasn't smart enough.

Grandma told me Mama had been hurt many times in her life and that's why she treated me so badly. She said to be patient with Mama and one day she would turn her life around. I wanted to believe her, but judging by Uncle Lee and TeeTee, addicts ran in the family and they seemed to be set in their ways.

Not long after, TeeTee walked in with a dazed look in her eyes. I knew she was high. I was sad to see how drugs had destroyed her toned physique, beautiful golden complexion and pearly white teeth. Now, her skin looked gray and her clothes hung loosely from her 5'7" frame.

"I smell fish," TeeTee said, looking through the empty bag Grandma left on the table.

"You better buy your own fish!" Granddaddy said, covering his food.

"Come on, Daddy. Don't be like that. Let me have a piece."

"No. Y'all always begging. Did you feed your kids today? I know they're hungry."

TeeTee puffed up, put her hand on her hip and said, "Don't worry about my kids, they're alright!"

"I am going to worry about your kids. They live in my house!"

"This is Mama's house, too! You get on my nerves with that!"

TeeTee stomped off, cursing, calling Meechie's name. "Meechie!"

"Yes!" Meechie called from the den in the basement.

"Did y'all eat?"

"Yes. I had Chinamen and Grandma gave Erin some fish," Meechie answered, standing at the end of the stairs.

"Your granddaddy seems to think I don't feed y'all," TeeTee said, rolling her neck and looking back at Granddaddy. The truth was she usually didn't feed Meechie and Erin. Grandma and Granddaddy did. Everyone knew TeeTee was on drugs, but nobody talked about it. I thought Grandma blamed herself for enabling TeeTee's habit, so she took care of Meechie and Erin out of guilt.

"You hear that? The only reason Erin ate is because we fed her. You're a sorry excuse for a mother," Granddaddy said under his breath.

"Whatever. Don't act like you're perfect. Remember, I got some dirt on you too." TeeTee crouched in his face. Granddaddy didn't say anything. He just looked at her, and continued to pick at his fish. Furious that she couldn't get a rise out of Granddaddy, TeeTee turned and walked out of the kitchen.

"Selfish ole' man," TeeTee muttered as she passed him by.

"That's alright. I'll be selfish, but I got a pocket full of money and you're broke!"

"Whatever!" TeeTee waved her hand and walked out of the dining room.

"What are you going to do about her, Rose?" Granddaddy questioned. "That child ain't been right since Lorenz died. She needs to go get some crazy pills or something."

Grandma's mood got somber. "She'll be alright. She's just going through something."

"She's going through something alright—everybody's pockets. I'm tired of it!" Granddaddy pounded on the glass-top kitchen table to show his frustration.

"What do you want me to do? Put her out?" Grandma asked.

"Hell yeah, if she going to be smoking that stuff."

"I rather she be here than out on the streets," Grandma reasoned.

"Rose, you can't keep blaming yourself for what happened to Lorenz. He made his own choices."

"I'm done talking. I'm going to get some sleep before I have to go to work." Grandma got up from the table and went to her room. Grandpa sat there for a while in silence, before heading out the door to stand on his favorite corner with his pals. I sat at the table and watched as my family transitioned in and out of the dining room. Eventually, the lights dimmed and the house grew quiet. I went downstairs and cleaned our room, just in case Mama came home. When I came back, Meechie was balled up on the couch in the living room while Lee and TeeTee were in and out of the house all night.

Sometimes, I slept on the couch because I didn't like being alone in our room. I laid on the loveseat and listened to Magic 108's Quiet Storm music on Meechie's Walkman. I imagined myself walking on an endless beach with André, hand in hand. My hair was blowing in the wind and wet from the warm tropical water. André pulled me close, looked in my eyes and reached for a kiss. It felt so real, I puckered my lips and waited for his lips to meet mine. Instead, I was startled out of my daydream by something crawling on my bottom lip, then across my cheek. I fanned my face and jumped up to find the culprit. There was a brown roach scurrying across the living room floor.

"Ewww, that's so nasty!"

Meechie sat up on the couch, "What?"

"There was a roach crawling on my face."

"Girl, you woke me up for that? I'm going back to sleep."

I hated roaches. Last year, Grandma had them really bad. Every time I turned on the kitchen light, I would see them running for cover. I remember Meechie killing a white one crawling across her dresser and twenty roach babies came out. A few months later, the exterminator came out and buried something in the yard. I hadn't seen one since—that is, before tonight.

Before lying down, I checked the couch for bugs and then Mama crossed my mind. When days had passed since I'd last seen her, I sometimes worried she'd been kidnapped or killed. I prayed she was okay, closed my eyes and drifted off to sleep. Before I knew it, morning had come.

I sat up on the loveseat and rubbed the sleep out of my eyes. After a good stretch, I made my way to the bathroom, but someone was in there. Meechie wasn't on the couch anymore, so I figured she was taking her sweet time in the bathroom. I knocked on the door and said, "Meechie, hurry up. I have to use it!"

"Meechie ain't in here!" a familiar voice called from the other side of the door.

The door swung open. It was Mama.

I perked up. "Hi, Mama! Where have you been?"

Mama frowned and snapped, "Out and about!" I looked at Mama, searching for sign of distress, but she looked well—like she had been relaxing for the last couple of days. Her hair was pulled back in a neat ponytail, she had on brand-new tennis shoes and her nails were painted fire-engine red. She didn't even look me in the face as she fussed. She just kept on walking. I walked behind her, hoping to get a few moments of her time.

"Well, I'm glad you're home. I don't have any clean clothes and there isn't any food here."

I no longer felt the need to pee. I wanted to tell Mama about my experiences over the last couple of days, but she hardly looked me in the face as she passed me by. I could tell Mama didn't want to be bothered with me, but I followed her to our room, rattling off as much as I could anyway.

Mama didn't like a nasty house, so I did my best to keep things clean. I figured if I made her happy, she would want to spend more time with me.

"Did you have a good night, Mama? I cleaned the room."

Mama didn't answer.

"Mama, these girls tried to jump on me the last day of school, but Meechie jumped off the bus and helped me. Then, the security guard broke it up. I thought we were going to have to fight our way out of there…"

Mama stopped me mid-sentence. "Look, I'm tired. Can we talk about this when I get up?"

"Okay." My shoulders collapsed.

I looked forward to spending time with her, but I silently hoped she would give me money so I could hang out with Meechie and her friends. For a moment, I wanted to feel free like a kid. I no longer wanted to worry about how I was going to eat or take care of myself while Mama was gone. I wished when Mama woke up that she would be different. You know, treat me as if she loved me. I felt like I could never talk to her about how I felt. She always ignored me or cursed me out.

"Is that all you need?" she asked.

"Yes." I looked at the floor.

"Well, turn off the light and close the door behind you."

I followed Mama's orders and left her alone. As I made my way up the stairs, I felt a deep sense of sorrow. I wanted Mama to love me, but I had no idea how to show her I was worthy. My 14-year-old brain couldn't make sense of her blatant disregard for my existence. *Why is she mad at me? Is it because the room isn't clean enough for her? I'll have to do better.* I prayed that Mama felt better when she got up. The stress of thinking about everything became too much. I began to worry. *If Mama doesn't give me any money, how am I going to eat? God, please help me. What am I going to do?*

CHAPTER

Four

I SPENT THE REST of the morning waiting for Mama to get up. Grandma's house was an old Craftman-style house with two bedrooms upstairs and a finished basement. Me and Mama shared a room in the basement, along with Uncle Lee. The kitchen was adjacent to the basement stairs. Therefore, if you were sitting in the kitchen, you could hear a mouse creeping up the steps. I sat at the kitchen table, hoping to get a glimpse of Mama before she disappeared again.

When I heard her footsteps gracing the stairs, I was excited to tell her about my plan to be more responsible. Mama departed the stairwell and entered into the kitchen, fully dressed in a blue work polo and neatly creased khaki pants. Mama worked as a cashier at a check-cashing place on West Florissant. She said she hated her job; that's why she needed to find a rich man to take care of her.

I cleared my throat, checked my courage and readied my mouth to express my newfound independence, but quickly became discouraged when I saw the frustration on Mama's face.

"I have to go to work, but I'll be back to get you. Be dressed."

I thought my dream had finally come true—Mama wanted to spend time with me. Elated, my body was erect and waiting to hear about our new adventure. "Really? Where are we going?"

Mama stood in the kitchen, digging in her purse. "We're going to spend the weekend at my friend's house."

"Oh."

My body sunk into the fabric of the chair. I wanted to spend time with Mama but, like always, she had something else to do.

While Mama talked about how great her friend was, I thought, "Here we go again."

There was always a new male friend she wanted me to meet. Mama had already been married twice in the past. Her first husband was an ex-military alcoholic who beat on her all the time. Her second husband was in the military, too. He seemed like a good guy, but Mama told me she divorced him because he was too jealous. *In a few weeks, her and this new friend will be fighting, and then she'll take it out on me.* I thought.

Feeling extremely irritated, I opted to tuck in my frown. I didn't want to upset Mama; I need some money.

"Okay, I'll be ready Mama." I took a deep breath and built up the courage to make my request. "Mama, can you leave me some money?"

Mama stopped at the mirror to apply her Passion

Pink lipstick.

"Girl, I don't have any money. Ask your Grandma."

"She told me to ask you."

Mama fluffed her shoulder-length tresses and gave herself an once-over in the mirror. "Oh, well. I guess you're going to have to find something in the kitchen." Mama didn't skip a beat as she headed to the door. "Be ready at five." She closed the door behind her.

I laid my head down and allowed my tears to form a puddle on the table. I knew the day was going to be long. More importantly, I knew I was going to be hungry.

"What am I going to eat?" Instead of panicking, I decided to wait until Grandma woke up to ask for help.

A few hours later, Grandma wandered into the kitchen, looking for her morning pick-me-up. No matter the time of the morning, Grandma always looked stunning. She was a beautiful Native American-looking woman who appeared to be decades younger than 52. I adored her. She was my favorite person in the world. I knew she loved me. She always protected and took care of me when Mama wasn't around.

"Good morning, baby. Did your mama come home last night?"

"Yes," I said, wiping the remaining tears from the corners of my eyes.

"Why do you look so sad?" Grandma sat next to me with her coffee in hand.

"My mama said she didn't have any money and there's no food here. She gets on my nerves. All she cares about is her friends and going out."

"I know, baby. Don't worry about it. Dry your eyes. I'll give you a couple of dollars."

Grandma went in her room and came out with a $5 bill. "Put this in your pocket and don't tell anyone I gave it to you."

Relieved, I put the money in my bra for safekeeping and instantly imagined how I was going to spend it.

"Mama said she was coming to get me after work."

"Really? Where y'all going?"

"Over to her friend's house."

Grandma didn't say a word, but the look on her face said a thousand of them. I could see she wanted to voice her disappointment, but felt she had no place to do so. After all, Grandma and Mama had similar stories.

In her youth, Grandma used her looks to get what she wanted. Grandma always thought the "Grass was greener on the other side," so she never stayed with one man for long.

Grandma and Granddaddy had been together on and off since before I was born. Despite her need to wander, he loved her. Therefore, he always took her back, pregnant and all.

Mama told me that, throughout the course of their marriage, Grandma had two children with two different men—TeeTee and my youngest aunt, Patrice. Out of her seven children, only Uncle Teddy and Lorenz were biologically his. Needless to say, Mama wasn't one of them. Her and her brother Michael were born from Grandma's first husband. Technically, Granddaddy wasn't my real grandfather.

For the rest of the morning, Grandma and me made small talk and watched soap operas. Instead of washing clothes, I decided to save my $5 and wash a few shirts and panties out by hand with dishwashing soap. I knew if I washed and hung them early, they would be dry by the time Mama got back.

I headed for the bathroom to wash my clothes in the bathtub. Meechie came in shortly after to be nosey. "Why are you washing out clothes? Where are you going?"

"My mama is taking me over one of her friend's houses."

"Is this the same one from last month who drove the Cadillac?" Meechie asked.

"No, I don't think she talks to him anymore. This is a new one." I rung out my clothes and temporarily hung them over the side of the tub.

"I hope this dude lives by André. I'm thinking about going to see him."

Meechie rolled her eyes. "You're still talking to him?"

"Yeah. Why?" I gathered my clothes and walked out of the bathroom and towards the front door. I laid the clothes on the front porch to dry in the hot sun.

Meechie followed. "He doesn't like you, for real. He just wants to hump you."

I giggled. "He's cool. He seems nice when I talk to him." I tried to hide my smile, but I couldn't.

"Of course he's nice to you, stupid. He wants to hump you," Meechie fired back.

"Meechie, g'on somewhere. You don't know what you're talking about," I chuckled.

"I heard he has a girlfriend. You better be careful; next time I ain't going to be there to save you."

He has a girlfriend? Meechie got my attention, but I intentionally ignored her by singing the ABCs in my head. While I laid my clothes out on the concrete porch, Meechie blabbered on like the adults in the Charlie Brown specials I watched when I was little.

After a few minutes, I drew my attention back to her, catching the end of her rant. "I'm just saying, be careful. I have a condom that Mr. Smith gave me in health class. Just in case you decide to be stupid and let him do it to you. He's probably got something." She frowned and folded her arms.

I busted out laughing. "I'm okay, Meechie. Calm down." She was so animated when she was frustrated; her arms flying everywhere, almost causing her skinny frame to fall over. "Come with me to the store."

"Hold up." Her neck rolled so hard her head almost flew off. "Where did you get money from?"

I wanted to tell Meechie, but Grandma swore me to secrecy, so I settled for a little back talk. "Girl, you ask too many questions. You coming or not?"

"I'll go, but you better buy me something," Meechie ordered.

Meechie and I walked to the convenience store a few streets from Grandma's house. Like Chang's, the local thugs hung out in front of the store. Cedric, the owner, did his best to get rid of them, but they always came back.

The only thing I didn't like about going was that you had to climb the slope on the side of the building to get there. Unfortunately, I'd seen many people fall coming down that hill in the snow, including me.

With my $5 I was able to get a few bags of penny candy, Sundance corn chips, and a pineapple Vess soda for me and for Meechie some hot fries. We headed back to the house to sit on the front porch and listen to music.

Time crept by and before I knew it, 5:00 was near. Realizing the time, I hurried and packed the shirts I washed and my last pair of clean underwear in my blue book bag. Luckily, Meechie wore the same size as I did, so she let me borrow some jeans for the day.

Around 5:30, I heard a horn outside. It was Mama. I said goodbye to Grandma and Meechie, grabbed my book bag and headed for Mama's red Pontiac.

"Hey, Mama. Did you have a good day at work?"

"Yeah, it was alright," she mumbled.

My attempts to engage Mama in conversation were failing miserably. I tried a new tactic.

"So…who is your friend?" Mama's face brightened and the corners of her mouth touched her cheeks.

"His name is Lawrence. I met him a couple of months ago. He's a nice guy. He has a son a little older than you."

"How old?"

"I think he's about 17 or so."

"Oh, okay."

"Me and Lawrence are stepping out tonight, so you and his son will be there together. I'll order a pizza or something before we leave. Oh, and I don't want any funny business." She took her eyes off the road long enough to give me a stare.

Disappointed, I spent the rest of the ride looking out the window. *She's always leaving me somewhere,* I thought. Mama paid me no mind though. She entertained herself by listening to Stephanie Mills and smoking a cigarette.

As we rolled through the city, I saw brown people sitting on their front porches and standing on the street corners. The city never rested. No matter the time of day, you could always catch people in fast food drive-thrus or staggering out of bars. On other nights, there was gunfire and the sound of ambulance sirens. Not all things about St. Louis were bad, but the poverty made people do what they had to do to survive. Even if that meant rob, kill or steal.

A short drive later, we pulled up to a brick, two-family flat.

Mama turned off the engine and double-checked her hair and makeup in the rearview mirror before getting out of the car.

I took my time walking up the steps to Lawrence's red brick row house. The porch was adorned with two mismatched chairs with soiled seats and a small round rickety table with a glass top.

"Be nice, Nikki."

Be nice? I thought. *I'm tired of faking like I'm happy. All she cares about is drinking and men. Besides, this will all be over in a couple of weeks. Like always.*

Although I thought meeting Lawrence was a complete waste of time, I nodded to acknowledge her demand.

Before Mama had a chance to ring the bell, Lawrence opened the door and greeted her with a hug and a kiss.

Mama's light-skinned face turned a bright red. "Baby, you are so crazy." She shooed at him with her hand. "Nikki, this is Lawrence."

"Hey," I replied, looking around at the ambiance.

"Hi, Nikki! I've heard so much about you." He held out his hand to greet me. I hesitated a few seconds then followed through with the weakest handshake I could muster.

Mama stood there proud, like I was her greatest accomplishment, but I knew better.

Lawrence looked a lot older than Mama. He had grey in his hair and wore funny glasses.

Lawrence extended his arm to a young man standing behind him in the doorway. "This is my son, Sean."

"Hey."

"Hey, how are you doing?" Sean was a cutie; tall, dark and handsome. I was confused how he came from his scrawny, four-eyed father. *He must be adopted.*

"Well ladies, let's go inside. Let me take your bags. Nikki, I'll put your stuff in Sean's room."

"Excuse the mess." Lawrence led the way through his house, pointing at the bathroom, kitchen and Sean's room on the way. His house looked like it hadn't been dusted in a while. Plus, it smelled stale and all the furniture was mismatched. I could tell a woman didn't live there.

I followed Sean into his room and stood by the door, using the dresser as camouflage. *Dang. I have to share a room with this boy all weekend? I hope he don't try anything.*

"Why are you standing by the door? Don't worry—you're safe. I ain't going to do anything to you, little girl," Sean chuckled.

Sean's room was neat and clean. He had a color TV and Super Nintendo in his room. Not to mention, a cordless phone.

"You have a phone in your room?"

"Yeah. You don't?" Sean replied, cleaning the clothes off his spare bed.

Yeah, right. I barely have clean clothes. I silently replied.

"Can I use it?" I asked.

"Yeah, go ahead." Sean pointed to the phone.

Since Mama was leaving, I figured I would call André to see what he was doing that night. I paged him and, like always, he called right back.

"It's for me!" I snapped, snatching the phone from Sean's hand. The last thing I wanted was Sean digging in my business. He looked like the type who would tell Mama I was talking to a boy. He was cute, but there was something about him I didn't like.

"Hello?" I said, out of breath.

"Somebody page me?"

"Hey, André. It's me, Nikki!"

"From where?"

"You know, Saints."

"Oh, what's up, girl? You going to Saints tonight?"

"No. I'm stuck over my Mom's friend's house."

"Where you at?"

"Somewhere by the Sears building."

"Is that right? The spot ain't far from the Sears building. You should come, though."

"Okay. Where is it?"

"On Euclid."

"Okay. When do you want me to come?"

"Whenever you're ready. Oh, and when you come, wear something sexy."

"Sexy?"

"Yeah. Why, you scared?"

"Nah, I'm not scared!"

I was petrified, but I couldn't let him know that. After all, he thought I was 16.

"Yeah, right. You're probably a virgin."

I lied, "No, I ain't."

"Well, come over and show me later."

"How do I get there?"

"Just call me when you're on your way and I'll give the directions."

"Alright. I'll call you in a little while."

My heart was beating so fast I could hardly breathe. Sean was sitting on his bed pretending not to hear my conversation, but he chimed in when I hung up the phone.

"How old are you?"

"Fourteen."

"You're a little girl. What are you doing talking to boys on the phone?"

"Dang, you're nosey! But if you must know, it's my boyfriend, André."

"I'm just trying to look out for you. You supposed to go and meet him or something?"

"Yes."

"He lives around here?"

"I guess. He said he's at the spot on Euclid Street."

"The spot, huh?" Sean smirked. "Do you know what 'the spot is', silly girl?"

"Of course. A place where guys hang out." I tried to sound confident, but I had no idea what happens at a "spot."

Sean took a deep breath and shook his head before debunking my myth. "The spot is where dope dealers sell drugs."

I felt stupid, but instead of admitting I was naïve, I put my hand on my hip and snapped, "I know. What do you think? I'm slow?"

"Actually, I do," Sean laughed. "How are you getting over there?"

"Walking, I guess."

"Walking? Little girl, you better be careful. It's rough over here."

"Rough? How do you mean?"

"You know, ROUGH. People get shot over here all the time, especially at night. Bullets don't have no names, you know?"

I was shaken, but I didn't care. My mind was on seeing André. I thought, *He'll protect me. This stupid boy don't know what he's talking about.*

"Why are you chasing after dope boys anyways? You know he has a lot of girls he's messing with, right?"

"No, he don't. You're just hatin'!"

"Hatin'?" Sean's face got serious. "Sweetheart, I go to school with most of these dudes, so I know how they get down. You're a cute girl. I would hate to see you get run through."

"Run through? What does that mean?"

"You know—taken advantage of. These cats don't care about you. He thinks you're a freak, that's why he invited you to the 'spot'. If you were his girlfriend, he would've invited you to this house." Sean laughed, "That's what's wrong with y'all St. Louis gals. Always chasing dudes because you think they've got money, but all you're going to get is a baby and a welfare check!" Sean shook his head and continued to sort through his clothes. "Little mama, you have a lot to learn."

Sean's words stung, but he was right. I was one of those stupid girls desperate for love and a chance to escape my life.

I have a lot to learn? What does that mean? I thought. I wanted to ask, but I knew questioning Sean would only prove I was young and dumb. André seemed like a nice guy. I couldn't accept that he would treat me that way…*would he?*

CHAPTER

Five

MAMA ORDERED THE PIZZA, and then got dressed for her date with Lawrence. Not long after the pizza arrived, I heard keys rattling down the hall.

I peeked my head out of Sean's door to catch a glimpse of Mama. She looked stunning in her white dress with spaghetti-sized tassels hanging from it. She completed her look with strappy, silver high heels and red full lips. She kind of reminded me of Tina Turner, without the big hair, but just as beautiful.

I wondered why she trusted Sean enough to leave me with him, while she and Lawrence partied. I guess, once again, men and booze meant more to her than me.

"We're gone. Be good, Nikki."

"Okay, Mama, I will." She gave me a side look before closing the door behind her.

I waited until I heard the ignition start and the car

pull off before I paged André.

A few minutes later, the phone rang. "Somebody page me?"

"Hey, André, it's Nikki."

"What's up, girl?"

"I'm ready to come over. Where are you?"

"Just come down Euclid. I'll be standing on the corner waiting for you. How long will it take you to get here?"

I put my hand over the phone and whispered to Sean, "How far is Euclid?"

"About ten minutes from here."

"I'll be there in ten minutes."

"Alright, cutie. I'll holla at you in a minute."

"Okay. See you soon."

I hung up the phone and rushed into the bathroom to get ready. I didn't have anything sexy, but I changed my shirt, brushed my hair and put on some lipstick that I found on the counter in Mama's makeup bag.

Sean sat on his bed cleaning his sneakers, watching me walk around in circles looking for my jacket.

"So, you're going through with it, huh?"

"With what?" I asked, putting my arm in my jacket.

"Going to see that boy?"

"Yep."

"I should tell your Mama."

Sean's threat got my attention. "Why do you care? You don't even know me."

Sean looked up from his task and flashed a crooked smile. "Don't worry. Your secret is safe with me."

"Whatever. Which way is Euclid?

"Just walk straight for six blocks and you'll run right into it."

I checked my ponytail once more and walked out the door. Once I closed the door, reality set in. *I'm in the hood.* There were abandoned buildings and people hanging on the corners, plus it was dark and creepy out there.

I walked quickly and looked behind me every 10 steps to make sure no one was there. I could hear the soundtrack of the city in my ears as my white canvas shoes hit the pavement—music playing, people talking and tires screeching. I was scared. I kept my head down, cautious to not make eye contact with anyone.

A few blocks down, I saw a group of men standing on the corner, drinking out of brown paper bags and offering customers small packs in exchange for money. I attempted to walk quickly past them, but my presence didn't go unnoticed.

"Hey, girl. Where are you going all alone? You need some company?" one man called.

I didn't respond but just kept on walking. My heart was racing as I prayed he didn't follow me.

"Hey! You hear me talking to you?"

I walked faster, stretching my legs as long as I could.

"I know you heard me, you stuck-up bitch!" I heard the man yell in the distance.

He reminded me of that time I walked to the store after dark to get something to eat. When I came out, there were four older boys standing at the end of the slope. I tried to go around them, but one boy with a grill of sparkly gold teeth blocked my way and insisted that

I tell him my name. I told him, but he wouldn't leave me alone. Finally I shouted, "I'm only 13!" and he eased up, but not before telling me, "You're going to be fine when you grow up. I'll be watching you."

Uncle Teddy told me to watch out for men like that because they liked to take advantage of little girls. I didn't understand why a grown man would want to have sex with a little girl. I just figured they were creepy that way.

I continued to walk as fast as I could to Euclid. I was so scared I wanted to cry. I'd never been out that late by myself. I wanted to go back, but that meant I would've had to pass that crazy dude on my way.

Instead of letting my fear get the best of me, I hummed a song and thought about how excited I was to see André. It seemed like forever before I reached Euclid. When I finally got there, I saw a familiar figure standing on the corner with a group of boys. As I slowly approached the corner, André walked towards me.

"You weren't playing, were you?"

"Nope. I wanted to see you."

André looked just as I remembered him, brown-skinned with a low haircut, hazel eyes and two gold teeth on each side of his mouth. He was dressed in a Nike t-shirt with jogging pants and white and black dope man Nikes.

He smelled so good, like my uncle's favorite cologne, Cool Water. I was so nervous I felt like I was on fire. My hands were super sweaty and my heart was beating a mile a minute.

"You're a cutie." He smiled.

"Thank you." The sight of his eyes intimidated me, so I looked down and kicked a rock that was minding its own business.

"Alright then, niggas." André gave his friends a pound, grabbed my hand and guided me to a big white house. He opened the door and locked it behind us.

"I'll be right back."

I stood nervously in the hallway as André briefly talked with a man sitting in a recliner and watching TV in an adjacent room.

"Alright, come on."

I followed his lead, up a dark staircase and into an empty room with a mattress on the floor and no sheet on it. I stood in the doorway, confused about what I was seeing.

"Why do you look like that? I thought you weren't scared?"

"I'm not." The truth is I was scared.

"Well, take off your pants."

I stood there, frozen. I didn't think he wanted to do "it." For some reason, I thought we would talk, and maybe kiss first. *Meechie was right. He did just want to hump me. I should've got that condom from her.*

I slowly pulled down my pants and hesitantly lay on the bare mattress. The room was dark, but I could see his white shirt reflecting off of the cars passing by. André dropped his pants to his shoes and climbed on top of me. I was stiff and frightened. I wanted to run.

He kissed me on my lips hard and short, spread my legs and then reached in his boxers to retrieve his manhood. I heard paper rattling. *Is he putting on a condom?* I was shaking; I didn't know what to expect.

Meechie told me when she and Eric had sex for the first time it hurt, bad. It was right after her thirteenth birthday. Eric's parents were like Meechie's other family. They trusted them alone. She told me the second time they had sex it wasn't as bad. I hoped that was the case for me, too.

I had seen sex scenes on TV, but they always seemed to be in love. There was always a lot of hugging and kissing. This was different; scary, even.

Instead of getting up and running, I decided to hold my breath and ready my body for the pain. It didn't take long.

André painstakingly attempted to put himself inside of me. Meechie was right: It hurt—bad. My first instinct was to push him off of me.

"Stop! It hurts!"

"Hold on, I'm trying get it in you."

"Ouch, ouch, please stop!"

André paused, "Wait. You're a virgin?"

I breathed, "Yes."

André stopped. "Why didn't you tell me?"

"I didn't think you would want to talk to me again."

Before André had a chance to respond, I heard the door open and saw a shadowy figure enter the room.

"Nah, man, get out."

"Nigga, let me get some."

"Nah, man, not this one! Close the door!" He closed the door loudly.

André returned his attention to me. "Do you want me to stop?"

"No." I figured, we had already started—so why stop now?

"I'll go slow, okay? If it hurts too much I'll stop."

"Okay."

André did his best to be gentle. He kissed my cheek and inquired if I was okay. I wanted to cry, but I held it in. I liked André, but in a way I felt robbed. I always thought that my first time would be on a nice bed, covered with roses, with the man of my dreams. Not on a stained mattress. I wanted the experience to be over. Scratch that...I wished it never started. After we finished, André took off the condom, wrapped it in its packaging and helped me to my feet. As I got dressed, he helped me find my shoes in the dark room and made sure I had all of my belongings before we headed down the steps and out the door.

Once outside, I prepared to say goodbye and head back to Lawrence's house alone. André surprised me.

"Can I walk you home?"

I was relieved, "Yes, please. It's scary out here."

"You should've told me you were a virgin. I wouldn't have let you come to the spot."

Damn, Sean was right. He thought I was a freak.

"I didn't want you to think I was a scared little girl."

"Why are you out at this time of night, anyway? Where's your mama? Does she usually let you stay out this late?"

"My mama is never home. Tonight, she went out with her boyfriend. I snuck out to see you."

André flashed his gold teeth and rubbed his head. "Girl, you're wild. It's not safe over here.

You better be careful walking around this time of night." He paused and grabbed my hand tightly before continuing. "Luckily, I'm here to make sure you're safe."

I smiled and looked down at the ground, attempting to conceal my bashfulness. I felt validated. André wasn't the jerk Meechie and Sean said he was; he did care about me. Even if it was only a little bit.

"Can I ask you something?"

"Yeah?"

"Do you have a girlfriend?"

André paused before answering. "Why do ask that?"

"I heard you had a girlfriend." I looked into André's eyes, searching for the truth.

"I did, but not anymore."

"What happened to her?"

"Shit, some gals don't want nothing but your money. She was one of them."

"So, do you have a lot of girls that you mess around with?"

André laughed. "Dang, you ask a lot of questions, don't you?"

"I just want to know."

"I have friends, but that's it." As André finished his sentence, something began to beep near his waist. He lifted his crisp, white t-shirt, revealing a small black gadget clasped to the side of his belt. After checking it, he continued, "You ain't got nothing to worry about.

Them gals don't mean nothing to me." André turned and put his arm around my waist and pulled me close to him. "I got to go. Give me a hug."

I obliged, hugging André tightly. He showed his gratitude by kissing me on the cheek.

"Call me when you get in the house."

"I will."

"Bye, cutie." André smiled once more before walking away. I watched his strut for a moment before turning to headed towards Lawrence's house. I could still smell the scent of André's cologne on my jacket. I didn't want him to go, but I knew he had someone waiting on him. Jealousy settled in my stomach as I thought of that "somebody" being a girl. I hoped I had showed André I was good enough to be his girlfriend and he wouldn't leave me like Mama does and my daddy did.

I wondered if he could tell I was young and vulnerable. *Did I act old enough*? I thought. While I recounted the night, I also thought of all the things that could've gone wrong. *What if that man would've killed me for ignoring him, or André would've let that boy come into the room?* I counted my blessings and thanked God for getting me home safe.

What a night, I thought, turning the knob to Lawrence's house and entering the darkness. *My God, what a night.*

CHAPTER

Six

THE HOUSE WAS QUIET. I didn't see Mama's car outside. I knew her and Lawrence were still out. I turned on the kitchen light to illuminate the dark hallway. I could hear Sean's radio playing in his room and the sound of light snoring between notes. I crept in his room to put down my coat and get my night clothes.

Before I had a chance, I felt something in my panties. Startled, I rushed to the bathroom and silently closed the door behind me. I pulled down my undies and sat on the toilet to investigate the sensation. *Blood? Why am I bleeding?* I wiped to examine how much blood was there. It wasn't much. It kind of reminded me of when I started my period the year before.

Mama wasn't there to help me, so Meechie had showed me how to use a pad and clean the blood out of my panties. I wiped myself two more times, then folded some tissue and put it in my panties to make a temporary pad.

My vagina was tender, but I didn't mind. The

sensation and the blood reminded me of André. I thought of the moment when he entered me, then the pain that accompanied it after. In some way, I thought the feelings I had for him would've translated into a beautifully romantic experience—like I'd seen many times in the movies. But it was different. So different, I didn't want to do it again until I was older.

The thought of someone coming in the room continued to haunt me. I also thought about André's reaction to the news that I was a virgin. I knew then, had I not told him, he would've allowed that boy to have sex with me or worse. Before allowing my emotions to get the best of me, I remembered my mission. I needed André to like me so he could rescue me from the misery Mama was forcing me to accept. I no longer wanted to be the arm piece she showed off to her potential beaus.

I also remembered Meechie telling me to be careful the first time I did it because I could get pregnant. I was relieved when André put on a condom; I knew I wasn't ready to be a mother. Still, I silently thought what it would be like to have a piece of André inside of me. *Would the baby look like him or me? Would he be a good father?* I rubbed my belly a few times and smiled, before the feeling of tiredness began to consume me. I wanted to call André, but I was too tired. Plus, I didn't want to wake Sean.

I'll call him in the morning.

I put on my t-shirt and shorts, made a pallet on the floor and closed my eyes. I took a deep breath and let out a sigh. Before I knew it, I had drifted off to sleep. I woke up to Sean rummaging around his room in the morning.

"Why are you making so much noise?"

"Because I can. This is my room. What time did you get in?"

"I don't know. Maybe about eleven o'clock."

"Hmmm, what did y'all do?"

I wanted to profess my womanhood, but I resisted. "Nothing. We just talked."

"Yeah, right. No boy calls a girl over to 'talk' at nine o'clock at night. I bet you gave him some."

"No, I didn't!"

"Why are you getting mad if you didn't do anything? You're a little freak." Sean couldn't contain his laughter.

"Whatever!" I rolled out of my makeshift bed and sat on the edge of Sean's bed.

"I should tell on you!"

"Please don't. Sorry for getting smart," I pleaded.

"Oh, yeah? How sorry are you?" Sean looked me up and down and smiled.

"Umm, not that sorry." I adjusted my shirt and wrapped the covers tightly around my frame.

"Ok, but you owe me."

"Y'all ready to eat?" Mama yelled from the hallway.

"Yes. Here I come, Mama!"

Mama and Lawrence must've had a good time last night. I could smell the delicious aroma of food filling the house. In the kitchen, there was a buffet of food displayed on the table—eggs, biscuits, fried potatoes and orange juice. I stared at the spread, then at Mama sitting at the table with Lawrence with a huge smile on her face. I was incensed at the fact that she went all out for Lawrence, but barely left me with enough to make a sandwich at Grandma's house.

"Wash your hands," Mama demanded.

I cleaned my hands in the kitchen sink and sat next to Mama.

"Go ahead and dig in," Lawrence cheerfully announced.

"No prayer?" I questioned.

"If you want to, you can. We don't follow that mess in our house."

I was taken back. *Dang, what they got against God*? I said a silent prayer to myself and piled some potatoes and eggs on my plate.

"So, what did y'all do last night?" Lawrence asked.

I almost choked on my food. I looked at Sean, praying he didn't expose me to Mama.

Sean answered, "Nothing much. We just listened to music. Nikki was on the phone most of the night."

After he completed his lie, Sean looked at me and mouthed, "You owe me." Then he smiled.

Mama turned and stared me down. "On the phone? With who?"

Sean had a smirk on his face. I wanted to kick his ass. "Nobody, Mama. Just a friend." I couldn't take my dagger-filled eyes off of him.

"It better not have been a nappy-headed boy."

"It wasn't, Mama."

"Keep on. Your little tail is going to end up pregnant. I ain't rocking no whiny-ass baby. I'm too young to be a grandma."

What does she care? She's never home anyway.

I sunk down in my chair, waiting for the scolding to be over. *Gosh, does she think I'm a hoe?* She would kill me if she ever found out about André.

Sensing my embarrassment, Lawrence cleared his throat. "Nikki, did you enjoy the pizza?"

"Yeah, it was okay." I didn't take my eyes off my plate.

"Your mother and I were talking about you guys and me and Sean getting together and doing something fun next weekend. Do you have any suggestions?"

"No, not really. Whatever y'all want to do is fine," I quickly answered.

"Ooh, I know," Sean interrupted. "We can go see that new movie, *Menace to Society*. I saw the previews. It looks like it's going to be good."

As Sean went on babbling about the movie, I faded out of the conversation. Eventually, his annoying voice took a backseat to my thoughts. I wasn't interested in playing family with two strangers. I wanted my real family back. Me, Sissy and Donny. We always had fun together.

When we were little, Donny would take me and Sissy to the Goodwill on Saturdays to pick out games. We would pretend to be on a scavenger hunt, looking for lost treasure.

I never went hungry and, most importantly, I felt loved. I wanted Donny to take me away from Mama, so me and Sissy could be happy like we used to be, but Mama told me Donny didn't want me. I knew I was stuck in St. Louis with her, unless I could find another way out. My heart began to ache at the thought of Donny not loving me anymore and at Mama choosing to love a stranger and his son over me.

I couldn't contain my pain anymore; I had to get out of there. "I have to go to the bathroom," I said, excusing myself from the table.

Before I fully entered the bathroom, tears were streaming down my face. I looked in the mirror at my sorrow and spoke to God. "Why doesn't she love me? What did I do?" I was so angry I vigorously wiped my face and clawed at my skin simultaneously.

The hurt I felt in my chest was so deep it couldn't find its exit. *No one loves me. She doesn't care about me.* "All she cares about is finding a damn man! I hate her!" I busted out of the bathroom and into Sean's room. My eyes were still red from crying. Sean came into his room and caught me wiping my face.

"What's wrong with you?"

I was silent.

"What?" He looked confused. "Are you mad because I told your mama you were on the phone?"

"No. Don't worry about it. It's none of your business."

"Alright then." Sean stood in the doorway for a moment, then turned and left.

"Nikki!" Mama yelled from the kitchen.

"Shit! That dumb boy told on me!"

Instead of responding, I quickly followed her voice.

"Yes."

"Get your stuff together. We're getting ready to

leave."

"Thank God!" I mumbled under my breath.

I packed my clothes and gratefully strapped my book bag across my left shoulder. I told Sean and Lawrence goodbye and anxiously waited for Mama outside. Lawrence walked her to the door. Before she exited, he hugged her tight and kissed her on the neck.

"Bye, baby. I'll call you later."

"Bye, Nikki. It was good to meet you."

"Bye."

I wasted no time getting in the car. "Why are you in such a rush?" Mama asked, throwing her purse in the back seat.

"I'm not. I just want to spend some time with you. You're never home. I—"

Mama cut me off. "So, you don't like him?" Mama let out a big sigh. "Why are you always ruining shit for me?"

"I'm not trying to. I...I was just saying..." I couldn't get a word in edgewise.

"Do you think I want to keep living at your grandma's house? I want my own place. I don't make enough money at the store, so I need someone to pick up the slack. Do you understand? Your triflin' ass daddy ain't no help. Look, Lawrence is a nice guy—try to like him. None of your funky ass attitudes. Got it?!"

"Yes, Mama."

We sat in silence before I made my request. "Mama, can I have some money to wash my clothes?"

"Damn, you always need something. Lawrence gave me a few dollars, so we can wash clothes later." I was thrilled. I hadn't had clean clothes in weeks. My socks were so funky and crusty they could stand up on their own.

Before going home, Mama made a stop at the corner store and came out with a slim brown bag in her hand. I knew Mama was getting ready to have some drinks. Sometimes, I liked it when she drank. It was the only time she hugged and kissed me.

Wait. I hope she doesn't get too drunk. How will I get to the laundromat?

"Are you going out tonight?"

"Why?" Mama snapped.

"I'm just curious."

Mama looked unnerved, like something was on her mind. She reached into the brown bag and pulled out a slim, white pack of cigarettes with the word "Capri" on it.

"Open these for me."

I removed the plastic wrapping from the pack and handed it to her. Mama pushed in the lighter and waited patiently for it to get hot enough to ignite her cigarette.

"I've got a lot on my mind. I'm going out for a little while. I'll be back to take you to the laundromat." Mama pulled up in front of Grandma's house and stopped in the middle of the street.

"Give me my purse."

I reached my arm into the back seat and retrieved Mama's brown leather bag.

"Here's $10. I'll see you later. Don't tell your grandma that I went out," Mama said, taking a drag of her cigarette.

"What time will you be back?"

"When I get back! Stop asking so many damn questions."

I wanted Mama to stay with me, but I knew she would just get mad or make up an excuse. Frustrated, I got out of Mama's car, slamming the door behind me.

"I know you ain't slamming my damn door!"

"Sorry, Mama. It was an accident."

"It better be!" Mama stared me down and drove off, leaving me standing in the street.

I watched Mama's car disappear down the street. Something in my gut told me Mama wouldn't be back. I wanted to cry, but I couldn't. I was fed up.

If Mama isn't going to be here for me, I'm going to find someone who will. I'm going to find my daddy.

CHAPTER

Seven

MAMA STUMBLED IN around 5:00 a.m., two days later. I heard her mumbling as she sat on the bed, plopping her shoes onto the concrete floor of the bedroom we shared. I knew Mama had been partying because the room smelled of alcohol and cigarettes.

I wanted to talk to her, but I settled for lying quietly and listening to her voice. I wondered what adventures she had been on that night. *Had she finally found the man of her dreams*?

I wanted Mama to be happy, but I felt that if she found a man, she would leave me like she always did. After hearing Mama ramble around for a while, the room was silent. I couldn't go back to sleep. I laid there and listened to Mama's snores and the sound of the crickets outside our window. It almost sounded like a fancy tune.

While I lay there, I thought about what my daddy looked like. I imagined the smile on his face when he saw me, and how it would feel when he hugged me. I was shaken out of my daydream by the sound of Mama's voice. "Nikki, go get me some water." I got out of the bed and shuffled around with my foot, looking for my house shoe to escape the coldness of the concrete floor.

"Hurry up!" Mama yelled.

Startled, I jumped up and ran up the stairs to get Mama a cold drink. When I returned, Mama was sitting on the edge of the bed.

"Thanks."

"You're welcome, Mama."

Mama drank the water and laid back down, pulling the covers over her head to let me know she no longer wanted to be bothered. I lay down and attempted to go back to sleep. I couldn't because the sun peeking through the blinds had an energizing effect on me. My body felt tired, but I couldn't sleep. Instead, I went outside, sat on the porch and watched the sun come up.

The city seemed so still. No cars were zooming down the block and no kids were hanging in the streets—it was just me. My head was filled with images of leaving St. Louis. I thought about asking Mama about my daddy, but I feared her reaction. All she ever told me was how he was a piece of crap. I expected the same or worse.

How will I get to my daddy? I don't even know where he lives. Even if I found him, how would I get there? Maybe, I'll get a job? It will take too long to save money. Who can I ask? I got it! André.

I snuck inside to look at the time on the stove. "Seven o'clock. Okay I'll wait until 10:00 to call him." I hadn't talked to André since the night after we did it. I paged him a few times, but he never called back. I wondered if Sean was right—had he just used me for sex? Ten o'clock came and I paged André. After 30 minutes, he didn't call back. I paged again. An hour passed and he still didn't call back. Furious, I called his house. No answer.

Is he ignoring me?

I sat by the phone for the rest of the morning, waiting for André's call. Every time the phone rang, I picked it up on the first ring.

"Hello, André?"

"No, is Lee there?"

"Hold on." I huffed and yelled Lee's name down the stairs.

I plopped myself in a dining room chair. Soon after, Meechie came in with a head wrap on and decked out in her favorite holey green housecoat.

"What's wrong with you now?"

"Nothing," I replied.

"It don't look like nothing is wrong with you."

I sighed, "I been paging, André but he ain't called back."

Meechie laughed and said, "Girl, please. That boy probably got two or three girlfriends. He ain't thinking about you. What, you think y'all go together?" She paused, and then laughed.

"Yep!" I retorted, rolling my neck and sticking out my lips.

"Girl, you stupid! Boys like that don't go with girls like you. Your booty ain't big enough."

"Yes, it is!" I got up out of my funk to show Meechie my butt. "See?" I showed her my little butt encased in my size 3 jeans.

"That little thing? Girl, shut up!"

"Whatever. He wasn't saying that when I saw him the other night." Realizing I said too much, I quickly covered my mouth.

Meechie stopped dead in her tracks. "What did you say?"

"Nothing."

"Yes, you did." Meechie looked me up and down. "Ooh, you did it with him, didn't you?"

I just looked at Meechie with a blank stare.

"When? You better tell me before I tell your mama!"

"I'm not telling you nothing!"

"Have it your way. AUNTIE!!"

"Alright, alright. Shhhh…! Yeah, we did it."

"I knew it! You a fast little girl, ain't you?" Meechie taunted me. "Did it hurt?"

"Yeah."

"What happened after?"

"Nothing. He walked me to Mama's friend's house and told me to call him."

"You haven't talked to him?"

I lied, to save face, because I knew Meechie would never let me live down the fact that she was right about André. "Yeah, a couple times."

"He probably has a girlfriend."

"No, he don't!"

"Nikki, wake up. André is a dope boy. All the girls like him. What makes you think he would choose you over girls with big butts and bamboo earrings? You still wearing yesterday's clothes."

"Because he said he likes me."

"Girl, you're stupid. Keep on waiting by the phone like

a dummy."

Meechie was right. André never called that day or the next. I had beeped him so many times, I finally gave up. *I guess he doesn't like me.*

Eventually, my hurt feelings turned into anger. I tore the paper André wrote his number on into little pieces. It didn't matter—I knew it by heart.

I hate him. I was stupid to have sex with him. What was I thinking?

Through the wee hours of the night, I laid in my bed listening to couples profess their love on the Quiet Storm radio show. I couldn't help but think about what our relationship could have been, as the sound of Keith Sweat's song, Right and a Wrong Way danced in my ears.

"I hate André. I hope he dies!"

I closed my eyes and, before I knew it, morning had come. I rolled over and sat up, looking for Mama in her bed, but she was gone. In the distance, I could hear the phone ringing. *André!* I zoomed up the stairs to catch it before the last ring.

"Hello!"

"You asleep?" the voice said on the end of the receiver. It was Keisha from around the corner. Meechie introduced her to me last summer. Keisha knew everyone; not to mention she also knew all the latest gossip.

"Nah, I just got up."

"You still talking to André?"

"Yeah. Who told you?"

"Your cousin, but never mind that."

"That damn Meechie, she talks too much!" I mumbled.

"Did you hear the news?"

"What news?"

"André got shot the other night."

"What? Is he alright?"

"Nikki....He's dead."

My heart stopped for a moment and shock took over my body. All I could do was hold the phone.

"Girl, stop playing!" My ears were ringing and my eyes were full of tears.

"I'm not. André and his cousins were on Euclid sitting in the car and somebody shot it up."

"How do you know it was him?"

"My cousin Joe is friends with Dré and his family. He told me. I tried to call you."

Damn, I thought. *Did I kill André? I mean, I was mad, but I didn't mean for him to die.*

"When did he get shot?" I asked Keisha.

"I'm not sure, but I think the other day."

The other day? That was the last time I spoke to him.

"Hello... Nikki, are you still there?"

"I'll call you back."

I hung up the phone and sat on the couch. *So, the whole time I was calling him, he was dead?* I felt horrible for calling him all of those names. All I could think about was André lying in that car, dead. *He seemed like a cool dude. Why would anyone want to do that to him?* I felt robbed. Someone had stolen my dream of getting away from Mama. *André is dead. What will I do now?*

In shock, I attempted to make sense of the news I just heard. *Keisha's wrong. I'm going to call.*

I picked up the phone, but hung it up. *What if he really is dead?* I took a deep breath, picked up the phone again and dialed André's number. The phone rang, once, twice, and then, on the third ring, a man's voice came on the line.

"Hello."

I paused and cleared my throat "Umm, is André there?"

"No, baby. André is dead. Please don't call here again."

"Okay." I slowly hung up the phone.

I felt bad that I no longer had André, but I felt worse for the man on the phone. He sounded broken and exhausted. It was clear he could take no more. My heart also ached for his mother. I couldn't imagine losing a child who was 17. I didn't know him that well, but he seemed to be a smart guy. I guess his only mistake was dope dealing and being in the wrong place.

I rushed into Meechie's room to tell her the news. "Meechie…Meechie."

"What do you want, girl? I'm asleep."

"André is dead," I whispered.

"What?"

"I said, André is dead." I raised my voice.

"How do you know?"

"Keisha just called me."

"How does she know?"

"She said her cousin told her."

"Girl, you know Keisha likes to gossip. She might have the wrong information."

"Nah, I called his house and his daddy said he was dead."

Meechie sat up in the bunk bed she shared with Erin. "For real? When did he get shot?"

"I don't know." I paused to wipe a tear running

down my cheek. "I guess a few days ago."

"Damn, that's messed up. You alright?"

"No. I didn't even get a chance to know him."

"Come on. Let's go outside." Meechie got out of bed and draped herself in her holey green housecoat and we headed for the front porch.

I sat in my usual place on the second step and Meechie sat next to me.

"You going to his funeral?"

"I don't know. Do you think I should go?"

"I would. At least to see him one last time."

I wanted to go, but I felt embarrassed. The only thing me and André had in common was him taking my virginity on a dirty mattress. I imagined his mother asking me how I met him and me responding, "We had sex a few nights before he died." What would she think of me?

"I don't even know his last name. How will I know when his funeral is?"

"I'm sure blabbermouth Keisha knows. We'll ask her," Meechie said.

"Yeah, how did she know I was talking to him anyway?" I knew the answer, but I wanted to see what she had to say.

Meechie looked guilty, as if she had done something wrong. "I told her."

"Meechie!" I fussed.

"What? I was trying to look out for you. But, that's not the worst of it..."

I turned my whole body to face Meechie. Her body language told me she was going to say something I wouldn't take lightly. "What did you do, Meechie?"

"I told Keisha that André didn't know how old you were and she told him."

"What! Meechie, why did you do that?"

"I didn't mean to. It just came out."

Me and Meechie had only fought one time before, when she said something nasty about Mama, but that day I wanted to punch her in the face. I caught myself, but the anger I felt was so intense, I had to get away from her. I jumped to my feet and walked down the three concrete steps that adorned Grandma's house. I stopped and turned before I reached the street. "Meechie, you know Keisha likes to talk. That was so stupid."

Meechie looked to her foot resting on the step. "Wait…there's more."

I walked towards Meechie. My heart was beating so hard, I had to sit down. I couldn't find the words, so I stared at her.

"Keisha told him how old you are," Meechie said slowly and softly. "So he was going to come and confront you, but I guess he got killed before he had a chance."

I put my hand over my mouth. *Is that why he wasn't calling me back?*

"Sorry, Nikki. I wanted to tell you, but I didn't know how."

No longer able to face Meechie, I walked away. I had just received the worst news of my life twice in one day. *Maybe this is God's way of punishing me for lying?* I walked around the neighborhood until my legs grew tired. When I came home, Meechie wasn't there and the house was quiet.

For the rest of the evening, I lay in my bed and

thought about André. His smile was imprinted in my brain along with visions of that night we spent together.

I wondered if the condom he wore actually worked. *I lost my virginity for nothing. I should've listen to Sean.* Then panic set in. *Oh, my God! I hope I'm not pregnant!*

The pain I felt ran deep. Feeling alone, I shifted into a tight ball until I no longer felt a void. I just cried. I was embarrassed that I put myself in that predicament, but angry at Mama for not being there. However, I knew if she ever found out about my mistake, she would jump at the chance to call me a 'hoe' and beat me.

I had no one to tell but God and myself. I looked under my mattress and dug out my journal. There had been so much going on over the last week, I had forgotten it was there. I knew my thoughts would be safe there. I could be vulnerable and share my true feelings. Plus, I always felt better when I wrote. I found a pen on the dresser next to Mama's bed and wrote until the pain I felt went away.

* * *

Dear God,

I'm sure you know that André is dead. I feel bad about wishing he would die. I pray that my wish to kill him isn't what made your decision. I hope you aren't punishing me for having sex with him. I'm so sorry, God, I will never do it again. Please take the pain I feel away. André, if you can hear me, I'm sorry that I lied to you. I hope you find peace in Heaven. I love you. Amen.

CHAPTER

Eight

Dear God,

It's been two weeks since I found out André was killed. His funeral was last week. I didn't go. All I could think about was seeing some girl crying for him. Keisha went. She told me there were a lot of people there. She said André's casket was open and he just looked like he was sleeping. I didn't want to see him that way anyway. I want to remember him the way he was when he walked me home that night. I miss his smell and the sound of his voice. I hope he's resting in peace. I haven't had my period this month. I hope I'm not pregnant. I know I'm too young to be a mother, but it would be nice to have a piece of André.

Last night, Mama told me we're moving soon. I'm happy we'll have our own place, but I know

I'll be alone. At least now when Mama leaves, I have Grandma and Meechie to keep me company. I guess we'll see what happens. Amen.

* * *

A FEW WEEKS HAD PASSED since André's funeral. Mama came home drunk one night and told me we were moving. I wasn't sure if it was the liquor talking or the truth. She surprised me the next day when she told me again. She said, "It's time we get out of your Grandma's house. I'm tired of her always questioning me about where I've been anyway."

I didn't want to leave Grandma's because I knew I would be fending for myself without the help of Grandma and Meechie. On the flipside, moving to the County meant better schools and peaceful nights. Since there were more white people there, it was safer. I wouldn't have to worry about getting robbed or ghetto-ass girls trying to jump me.

I damn sure didn't want to go to Beaumont Senior High next year. Sophia and the G-Gs were going there. That meant the potential for me getting my ass kicked by them was greater. The boys in the County looked better, too. They weren't all dirty and rowdy like the city boys. Most of them came from good homes, with parents who actually gave a damn about if they ate that day.

Although apprehensive, I tried to find the silver lining. *Since we're moving into our own place, Mama will be happier.*

We can spend more time together. But even my wildest visions of me and Mama getting to know each other seemed foreign. She wasn't the cuddly type.

A few weeks passed and it was finally moving day. I finished packing the last of our stuff and sat down for a break before Mama came back with the moving truck. I heard the stairs squeak and the light patter of someone's feet. "Nikki Pooh?" a voice whispered from outside of the door.

"Grandma?"

"Yes, baby. What are you doing?" Grandma came in and sat next to me.

"Trying to finish packing before Mama gets back."

"Are you happy to be moving?"

"Kind of. I'm happy that I don't have to go to Beaumont next year."

"Yea, I think the County will be a lot better for you. Listen, if you ever need me you call me, okay? I know how your Mama can be."

"I want to move with Mama, but I'm scared. I'd rather stay here with you."

"I know you do, baby. Your mama means well but she's under a lot of stress."

"Is that why she's always gone?"

"Maybe."

"Why does she act like she doesn't want me? All she cares about is getting drunk and chasing men. The only time she's nice to me is when she wants me to pretend she the perfect mother to her guy friends."

"Don't say that, Nikki. Your mama loves you. She just has a hard time showing it."

"Yeah, but she can hang out with her 'friends'

though."

"Give her a little time, baby. She'll come around."

"You always say that, Grandma, but she never does. She leaves me without money to get food or wash my clothes all the time. I'm tired of being called dirty and being yelled at because I'm hungry. Please, Grandma, let me stay. I don't want to go with her," I vented.

"Listen, calm down. Everything will be alright, okay? Here, take this money." Grandma handed me a neatly folded $20 bill. "Don't tell anyone I gave that to you. I wish I could do more, but I know you'll be alright. You're a smart girl."

"You ready?" Mama yelled down the stairs.

"Yes, Mama."

"Give me a hug," said Grandma. I didn't want to let go. I loved her so much I wanted to show her with every second I held onto her. "I love you, baby. Remember what I told you."

"I love you, too, Grandma. I will."

Mama and me moved all the boxes, while Lee sat in his favorite chair and supervised.

"Y'all are so weak."

"Then why don't you help?" Mama fired back.

"If you give me $10, I will."

"Boy, please. I ain't giving you nothing."

"Well, I ain't helping you with NOTHING."

Mama rolled her eyes and sucked her teeth. "Ole crackhead ass."

We loaded the truck as full as we could and took off on our journey to the County.

The County was the suburbs of St. Louis. Everyone wanted to leave the city to live there. Plus, the schools were better.

In the County, you had your pick of good schools: Riverview Senior High, Hazelwood West and Parkway North. Upper middle-class families usually lived in the County. I loved the County. It looked so clean. The grass was greener, the trees were taller and the people were friendlier, too. In many ways, it reminded me of Washington.

"We're almost there," said Mama, smiling.

It had been a long time since I saw her smile. I was glad to see her happy. As we made the left turn into the apartment complex, I read the sign: "Countryside Apartments." They were nice. No one was hanging on the corner or gathering in the street. The lawns were well manicured and the building looked freshly painted. *Maybe living with Mama won't be that bad after all.*

"We're here." Mama stopped the truck in front of a tan door adjacent to a green bush beautifully adorned with pink flowers.

"We're home. What do you think?"

I opened the car door and stepped out in amazement. "It's nice!"

"I'm happy you like it. Come on. Let me show you the inside."

The townhouse looked new, like we were its first owners. The carpet was fluffy and it smelled like fresh paint.

"Here's the living room, kitchen and bathroom. Those steps go to the bedroom. For now, you and me will have to share a room like we did at Grandma's."

I followed the stairs to their end and found myself standing in a large room with a small bathroom with a shower. I stood in the middle of the room and imagined me and Mama finally getting a chance to spend time together.

I realized that I'd known Mama for all my life, but didn't know anything about her. She was a mystery. I didn't know what her favorite color, food or dream was. I wanted her to share her thoughts, fears and joy with me, but something in my heart led me to believe things would soon fall apart. *I'm going to give her a chance like Grandma told me. Maybe she'll change?* I cast my final wish then went downstairs to find Mama. She'd already begun unloading the truck. "I was wondering if you got lost. It took you long enough."

"I was just looking around. I like this place."

Mama flashed a smile. "Come on. Let's unload this truck before it gets dark."

It took an hour to unload the truck. When we were done, Mama treated me to Chinese food. We sat and ate together on the floor of the empty dining area.

"So you like the apartment, huh?"

"Yes, it's nice. What school will I be going to?"

"I don't know. I'll have to find out before school starts in September."

Mama paused for a while before continuing. "You know I want the best for you, right?"

Her sincerity got my attention. "Yes."

"I know I'm not home all the time—I want to be. I'm trying really hard… Just let me work a few things out, okay?"

"Why did you leave me all the time? Did I do something wrong?"

"Look… I said let me work things out." Mama got up and headed to the kitchen to throw away her trash.

"But—" I tried to reason.

"Sweetheart, I'm dealing with some things I don't think you can understand." When her eyes began to well up with tears, she turned her back to conceal her emotions. But I saw her wipe her eyes with the top of her shirt.

"Where's my purse?"

My heart began to race. "Mama, I'm sorry. Please don't leave."

"I'm not leaving…" She fussed, pulling her cigarettes from her brown bag. "What's wrong with you?" Mama cut her eyes at me and walked out the door to smoke. Mama seemed depressed. I wanted to ask her, but I knew in my heart that she would never tell me. I watched her through the window, smoking her cigarette and staring off into nothingness.

When she came in, she swooped past me saying, "Good night." Then, she went up the stairs and closed the bedroom door behind her. Too afraid to bother her, I balled up on the fluffy living room carpet, and closed my eyes until I fell asleep.

The next morning, Mama wasn't there. I found a note on the kitchen counter that read: "Had to go to work. See you later." I opened the fridge. It was empty—the cabinets were too. I started to panic, but I remembered the money Grandma gave me.

Good thing Grandma gave me that money. I guess I have to go to the store.

I put on my shoes and walked through the

neighborhood in search of a store. I didn't have a key, so I left the door unlocked and prayed no one was there waiting for me when I got back. Once I got to the main road, I noticed there was a corner store a few blocks down.

I got some milk, cereal and a snack for later, then headed back. On my way, I saw little kids playing and people sitting on their porches. I didn't see any kids my age. I hoped they would come out later.

I spent the rest of the day waiting for Mama to come home, but she didn't. Days passed and I kept myself company by watching old reruns of *The Cosby Show*. I imagined what it would be like to have Claire and Dr. Huxtable as my mother and father. They seemed so happy and loving towards their kids.

On the third day, the money Grandma gave me started to run out, so I began to worry. I noticed there was hardly any food in the refrigerator and the lunch meat and noodles I bought were getting low. "What am I going to do?"

I tried to make a plan, but had no idea where to start. I hated when Mama left me. I always ended up having to figure how to take care of myself. *Why does Mama do this shit?*

I closed the refrigerator and kicked it on my way out of the kitchen. "Ugh!" I screamed. The sound of my voiced echoed throughout our empty apartment. I thought of Grandma's voice asking me to be patient with Mama, and it calmed me. I sat in the middle of the living room floor, trying to reason with the rage I felt inside. *I love her so much, but I'm tired of this. She won't change. I should run away and find my daddy.*

The constant worry and anxiety began to have a physical effect on my body. My skin was full of bumps, my stomach was in knots and I was having constant headaches. I knew something had to change, but I just didn't know what. Grandma told me when times were tough to pray to God. I wasn't too sure that God listened to me, but it was worth a shot. Plus, writing always made me feel better. I pulled my journal from my backpack, sat on the bedroom floor and began my plea to the creator.

* * *

Dear God,

Mama hasn't been here in days. Luckily, Grandma gave me that money. I don't want to live with Mama anymore. Please help me find my daddy. Mama says he doesn't care about me, but I know if he knew what was going on he would take care of me. Will you tell him I'm looking for him? Or, at least, tell me where he is so I can find him? Please God, any clue will help. I'm counting on you. Amen.

CHAPTER

Nine

THE NEXT MORNING, I heard the front door open and close. *Mama's here. Thank you, God!* I jumped out of bed and ran down the stairs to meet her.

"Hey, Mama."

"Hey," she said, passing by on her way to the kitchen.

I was puzzled. She acted as though she hadn't just left me for four damn days without food. I knew she'd been out partying all night because she smelled of her usual alcohol and cigarette stew, her face was still full of makeup and she had on a fancy, shimmery black dress.

"Where have you been, Mama?"

"Nikki, what did I tell you about asking me where I've been?"

I put my head down and mumbled, "But there's no food here."

"What did you say?" Mama kicked off her shoes,

threw her purse on the counter and opened the fridge. "What happened to all the food I bought?"

"There wasn't anything but the cereal, milk and noodles I bought."

"Yeah, right. There was more food here than that." At that moment, I began to see how drinking and partying were killing her brain cells. *What is she talking about? She ain't bought any food since the day we moved in here. Is she going crazy?*

Mama turned to me and squinted her eyes. "Who did you have in my house?"

"Nobody."

"Yeah, right, little girl. You think I'm stupid, don't you? I know your ass is screwing. Look at your titties filling out. You ain't pregnant, are you?"

Oh, my God, how does she know I had sex? Do I look pregnant? When Mama turned her head I gave myself a once-over. My period was supposed to come on the 20th, but I didn't feel pregnant.

I knew I could never tell her what happened with André. She would rip me to shreds. "I'm not having sex. Who told you that?"

"Ain't nobody had to tell me nothing. I know a little fast-tail heffa when I see one."

I stuttered, "Well… I ain't having sex and I'm not pregnant." Mama's assumption had me spooked. *Damn, I hope not.*

Mama stared at me as if she was looking for untruths in my essence then closed the fridge and opened a cabinet. I stood behind her, hoping she would come to her senses. As she closed the cabinet and began to walk away, I found the courage to stop her. "Mama…"

"What do you want, Nikki?" she asked with her hand on her curvy hip.

"I'm hungry. Will you take me to get something to eat?"

"Girl, there's plenty here to eat. Make a sandwich."

"There's no bread or meat."

She pointed at the cereal box on top of the refrigerator. "Eat some cereal."

"There's not enough milk."

"Nikki, I ain't got time for this shit. Figure it out."

The scent of White Diamond perfume, cigarettes and alcohol filled my nose as she passed me and headed up the stairs.

Tears filled my eyes. "I hate you!" I yelled within. My stomach growled with hunger. Now, what was I going to do? The only person I could think to call was Grandma, but I didn't even have enough money to use the payphone. *I'll just take some change from her purse. She won't miss it.*

I looked on the counter for Mama's purse but couldn't find it. She took it upstairs with her. I opened the closet door and found her coat. I quietly checked the pockets, but all I found was a coat check ticket, and a piece of paper with the name "David" and a number written on it. *Damn!* I let out a big sigh. I knew I had to ask her for money. I sat on the floor for a while, thinking of my strategy.

I could hear Mama thumping around upstairs and talking to herself. I waited until she settled down before I climbed the stairs behind her.

When I came upstairs, she was laying on the bed,

watching the news and smoking a cigarette. She seemed unsettled, like something was on her mind. The deep breath she let off as I entered the room told me I wasn't welcome. I sat on the bed next her anyway.

"Why Clinton sending them boys over to the Middle East? I bet Bush had something to do with it. I can't stand Bush's ass. He ain't did nothing for black folks," she ranted.

"I thought you liked Clinton?"

"He's alright." She took a drag of her cigarette and let out a chain of smoke.

"Mama, whatever happened to Lawrence?" I asked, fanning the excess smoke out of my way.

"Who?"

"You know—the guy whose house we spent a night at with the son?"

"Oh, I left his old stingy ass alone. He wasn't talking about nothing anyway."

I paced my conversation with Mama. I knew if I came out and asked for money, she would get upset.

She seemed to be amused by the show she was watching, so I waited until she laughed to ask my question.

"Mama."

"What?"

"Can you give me a few dollars to call Grandma?"

"For what?"

"I want to say 'hi' to Grandma."

Mama took a drag of her cigarette. "What are you going to tell her?"

"Nothing. I'm just going to talk to her."

"Talk to her? Ha! What could you possibly have to

talk about?"

"You know, stuff."

"Hmmm."

"Please, Mama! You're always gone. I don't have anyone to talk to."

"Yes, you do!" she sat up in the bed. "Talk to Jesus." She chuckled, then reached for the nightstand and put out her cigarette.

"I don't have any money. Do you think it's free to live here?"

"Not even any change?"

"I said I don't have any money, Nikki! What you can do is get out of my face before I knock your ass out. And if you do talk to your grandma, you better not tell her my damn business."

I got up and rushed down the stairs. I can't stand her! *Why does she love to make my life miserable?* I thought. I wished I was big and strong enough to beat Mama up. The rage I felt turned into tears.

"You stumping?" she yelled down the stairs.

"No."

I could hear Mama's footsteps coming down the stairs. She didn't waste any time making her point.

"You got something to say to me?" She wrapped herself in her blue housecoat and tied the belt in a loose knot.

"No, Mama," I said, tears rolling down my face.

"It looks like you've got a problem, to me. G'on head. Say what you got to say."

"…I'm just hungry Mama. There ain't nothing to eat here."

"Shut up with all that damn crying. You're old

enough to take care of yourself."

"But, Mama you're always leaving with no money—" She cut me off. "And you ain't died yet, are you? You know what? I'm sick of your ass! You always need something. If you don't like how I run my show, you can leave."

"Where am I going to go?"

"Shit, the hell if I care. Your no-good daddy don't want you. Call your grandma. Tell her nosey ass to come and get you."

"I don't have any money."

"Mary lives around the corner. Go use her phone. I don't care where you go. Get your ass outta my house."

I stood there frozen. I wanted to leave, but I was afraid to.

"What's your grown ass waiting for? Bye! Get your shit and leave!" Mama pushed me hard in the middle of my chest, causing me to lose my balance and fall on my butt.

"But, Mama…"

"I said get out!" Mama raised her arm, but before she could hit me, I ran out of the door. She slammed the door behind me. Tears filled my eyes, but I didn't let them drop. I took a deep breath then regrouped.

I had been over Mary's house once before, but I didn't know what direction she lived. I remembered she had a flowerpot on her porch with pink flowers in it. If I walk around the neighborhood, I could probably find her house.

I walked around for hours until I saw a flowerpot with beautiful pink flowers in it. There was a car parked out front. I walked up to the door, but before I knocked, I put my ear to the door to see if I could hear anything. I could hear music playing. After walking two hours to find her house, I got cold feet and almost left. Instead I made a deal with myself to count to ten and ring the bell.

"Seven...Eight...Nine...Ten." I rang the bell and stood there practicing my smile in the glass of the door. All I could hear was Mama's voice telling me not to tell anyone her business.

My plan was to ask to use the phone to call Grandma. If she asked anything, I would say, "I don't know." Just as I was finalizing my plan, the door opened.

"Nikki?" she said, looking around.

"Hey, Aunt Mary. Can I use your phone?"

"Sure you can. Come in. How did you get over here?"

"I walked."

"From the city?"

I chuckled. "No, me and Mama live around the corner."

"Y'all don't have a phone?" Aunt Mary asked as she led the way to the kitchen.

"No, not yet."

"Well, what will you do if there is an emergency?"

"I don't know. Go and get help, I guess?"

She looked at me with discontent. "You guess? Nikki, you be careful around here. There are crazy people out here kidnapping kids and stuff." Mary pointed to a green phone on the kitchen wall. "Do you want something to drink?"

"No, thank you."

"Have you eaten?"

I shook my head 'no' and focused on the phone ringing.

"Hello?"

"Grandma?"

"Nope."

"Meechie?"

"Yep. Who is this?"

"Nikki."

"Hey, girl. You still mad at me?"

I missed Meechie. I was happy to hear her voice. I wanted to tell her everything, but Aunt Mary was staring down my throat.

"No. I don't care about that anymore."

"Good, cause I don't care if you're mad anyway. I miss you. When are you coming over?"

"That's why I was calling. Is Grandma there?"

"Nope. She ain't here. I think she went shopping or something."

"Alright. Tell her to call me over Aunt Mary's when she gets home."

"Alright."

Before I could say anything else, she hung up.

"You never told me what you wanted to eat," Aunt Mary reminded me.

"Do you have cereal?"

"Yes. Give me a second and I'll make you a bowl. Were you able to get a hold of your Grandma?"

"No. She wasn't there."

"She's probably on her way over here. We're

supposed to go look at some shoes. You can stay here until she comes if you want."

"Okay. Thank you."

It felt good for someone to be nice to me. I didn't know Aunt Mary too well. Her and Grandma were the closest out of their siblings, but she didn't come around much.

What I loved about Mary was she wasn't afraid to be herself. Her signature look was spandex pants with stockings and high heels. I bet she was a bad mama jama back in her day.

"Here you go. I hope you like Cheerios."

"That's fine." I was so hungry I would've eaten the box if she served it to me.

"Dang, child. When's the last time you ate?"

"Umm, a little while ago," I lied.

"Where is your mama?"

"At home."

"Why she didn't come with you?"

"I don't know." I wanted to tell Aunt Mary what happened, but I was afraid. She'd tell Mama and make things worse.

For the next hour, Aunt Mary tried to engage me in conversation, but I was mindful about what I said. I was relieved when Grandma got there. "Nikki, what are you doing here? Give me a hug!"

"Hi, Grandma." I hugged her so tight I didn't want to let go. She looked down and whispered, "Is everything alright?"

I wanted to break down in tears and tell her everything, but I didn't. If she knew Mama was leaving me home with no food, she would get upset. I fought back my tears, but secretly hoped she would still see my pain. "I'm okay, Grandma. I just wanted to see you."

"Are you sure?"

I hesitated. "Yes."

"Well, take off your jacket and stay awhile."

The rest of the visit was a blur. Grandma and Aunt Mary chatted and drank coffee. I sat there and pretended to listen, while I thought about how I was going to tell Grandma that Mama put me out.

"Nikki, are you okay?"

"Yes. I'm just a little tired."

"Where's your mama?"

"She's at the house."

"Do you have money in your pocket?"

"No."

She reached into her purse and pulled out a $20 bill. "Here, spend it wisely." I needed the money, but I wanted Grandma to take me with her more.

"Mary, are you ready? We'd better go before the stores get crowded. Nikki, do you want us to drop you off?"

"Umm…"

"What is it, Nikki Pooh?"

"Grandma, can I go with you?"

"Why? What's going on?"

I took a deep breath and was about to tell Grandma everything, but then I didn't, "Nothing." I smiled. "I just haven't seen you in a while."

"Oh, baby. Me and your aunt have plans this weekend. I can come and get you next weekend though."

"Okay."

"You want me to drop you off?" she asked once more.

"No, I'll walk."

Grandma hugged and kissed me on the cheek before getting in the car. "I love you, Nikki Pooh."

"I love you, too, Grandma."

"If you ever need to use the phone again, you come see me. Okay?" Aunt Mary said as she reached for her seatbelt.

I watched them drive off. I wished I could go too. I knew I had messed up my opportunity to get away from Mama. "Why didn't I tell her?" I mumbled to myself.

I wished Grandma could read my mind. I hoped she would feel something in her spirit that prompted her to come back. But, she didn't. I walked home to find Mama's car outside, but the door locked. I rang the doorbell and knocked for hours, but Mama never came to the door. As the sun rose, the rays from the sun began to leave their mark on my golden-brown skin. The humidity was tortuous. The thirst that followed was worse.

My stomach began to cramp and I felt something wet in my panties. I looked between my legs and saw a huge red spot in the center of my shorts. I was thankful to start my period, but even more desperate to get inside. I rang the bell and banged on the door and yelled for Mama.

"Mama, please let me in!"

She let me stay outside for twenty more minutes before opening the door. "I knew your pitiful ass would come crawling back," she taunted me. "Get in here."

Happy to escape the heat and get something cool to drink, I hurried in the door. Blood was running down my leg and into my shoe. I ran into the bathroom to clean myself and wash out my panties.

"Mama, I need some pads. I started my cycle."

I heard silence, then the door opened and a handful of maxi pads wrapped in pink plastic pouches came flying my way.

"That's all I have. If you run out, you're on your own." Then the door closed.

I sat on the toilet until my legs got numb. Afterwards, I washed the blood out of my clothes the best I could and hung them over the rack on the back of the toilet to dry. I was happy to find a pair of underwear and sweatpants in a box. I stayed away from Mama for the rest of the day.

I'd never seen her be that mean but something told me things were about to get a lot worse.

CHAPTER

Ten

Dear God,

Mama just told me Sissy is coming for the summer. I'm excited! I haven't seen her in a long time. I hope Mama will stay home more since Sissy will be here. Maybe Sissy and me will play games and talk like we did when we were younger. I can't wait to see her tomorrow. Thank you for listening, God. Amen.

* * *

THE NEXT DAY ME AND MAMA went to pick up Sissy from the airport. Mama seemed happy, but I noticed she was smoking more cigarettes than normal.

"I hate coming to this damn airport! I can never find where I need to go."

"What airline is she coming in on?" I tried my best to help Mama navigate as she sped past the airline names.

"Delta, I think."

Mama parked her car under the Delta sign, hoping to catch a glimpse of Sissy. A police officer standing by approached Mama's car and tapped on the passenger-side window.

Mama rolled down the window and flashed her prettiest smile. "Yes, officer?"

"Umm, ma'am, you can't park here. This lane is for dropping off and picking up only."

"Alright, sir." Mama waited to roll up the window before she expressed her frustration. "Goddamn police always messing with folks! Go inside and see if you can find Sissy. And hurry up! I don't have gas to be driving around in circles."

I sprang out of the car and ran through the automatic doors, dodging a few people moving too slow for my stroll. I was sure Sissy would look the same—tall, dark-skinned with a ponytail. Sissy always slicked her hair back into a ponytail because she didn't know how else to style it. I wondered if she still had the burn on her forehead from the last time she attempted to curl her hair.

Sissy was three years younger than me. She was sweet and smart. Donny kept her busy with cultured activities, such as chess and debate club. She also played the violin in an orchestra. One year, she got to play at the White House. I was jealous that Sissy had a good life, with a father who cared for her. I knew that St. Louis would eat her up if it had its chance. I wouldn't let it. Her innocence motivated me to look after her. I enjoyed being the older sister.

I looked all over, but I couldn't find her. Finally, I gave up searching and asked a man pushing a cart full of luggage where to go. I stood at baggage claim, anxiously waiting for Sissy. *What if she's changed so much that I don't notice her?* I scanned the crowd, looking for an older Sissy, but couldn't settle on anyone.

"Nikki!" I heard a familiar voice call out. I turned around and there was my sister.

"Sissy!"

I hugged her tightly and gave her a kiss on the cheek.

"Where's Mom?"

"Mom?!?" I laughed hysterically. She spoke so proper. I hadn't heard that accent in a long time. "She's driving around waiting for us to come out."

I looked Sissy over once before I helped her with her bags. She looked well taken care of. Her clothes were clean, her hair was neatly pulled back in a ponytail and all of her luggage matched. She wore a pair of yellow headphones around her neck like they were accessories.

"Come on. We better hurry up before Mama loses her mind." I grabbed Sissy's hand and pulled her outside to the curb. A few moments later, Mama drove up, got out of the car and ran and hugged Sissy.

"Hey, baby! How was your flight?"

"It was fine."

"Good. Let me help you with your bags."

Mama was different. She was smiling and acting super nice to Sissy.

"Nikki, let Sissy sit in the front so we can talk."

What? Why can't she talk to her from the back seat?

Mama and Sissy talked all the way home. Mama had never talked to me that much. When she did, she yelled and told me to get out of her face. I was jealous and mad that she was putting on a show for Sissy.

"Are you hungry, Pumpkin?" she asked Sissy.

"Yes, Mom."

"What would you like?"

"Umm, tacos."

I sat up. "No, Mama! I hate tacos."

"Nikki, shut up! Nobody asked you what you liked."

I sighed and rolled my eyes. "I can't stand you!" I retorted under my breath. I couldn't stop thinking about how happy I was going to be when I found my daddy. I knew he would never treat me like dirt and leave me alone.

Mama and Sissy kept babbling in the front seat until the car stopped. When they got out of the car, I lingered behind, rallying against Sissy's food choice.

"You're not getting out?" Sissy asked, passing by my window.

"Yes," I mumbled and rolled my eyes, wishing Mama could feel it. I got out of the car and followed Mama and Sissy into the restaurant.

While she and Sissy studied the menu, I leaned against a table, trying to recover from the smell of fake meat and nacho cheese.

Mama knows Mexican food makes me sick. Why would she make me eat here?

"Do you know what you want, baby?" Mama was still talking to Sissy.

"Yes. I want two tacos, please."

Her tone changed. "Nikki, what do you want?"

"I don't know. Mexican food makes my stomach hurt."

"Girl, you better order something. I ain't stopping nowhere else."

"But, Mama…"

"You better pick something, unless you want to starve tonight."

How would that be any different from any other night? I thought.

I looked at the menu, hoping to find something appealing, but couldn't. Eventually, I settled on nachos. I knew I would be on the toilet all night. After getting our food, we headed back to Countryside.

When we walked into the townhouse, the look on Sissy's face told me she wasn't used to the way we lived. In Washington, Sissy had her own room, full of dolls and decorative pink wallpaper. Sissy stood in the doorway for a few seconds before coming in and dropping her duffel bag on the floor.

"Where's the table?"

"We don't have one," I told her, trying to hide my sarcasm.

"Well, where do you eat?"

"On the floor."

"On the floor?" Sissy looked puzzled. "Okay."

We sat on the living room floor and ate our food. Mama didn't bother to eat with us. She headed upstairs. I could hear the shower running. Soon after, I heard her singing. She only did that when she was getting ready to leave. I felt bad for Sissy. She had no idea what she'd walked into. I thought for sure that Mama would be home while Sissy was in town. I was wrong.

The smell of White Diamonds wafted through the apartment. "Who's spraying perfume?" Sissy asked.

"Mama."

"Is she going somewhere?"

"Yep, out." I tried to mask my frustration as I regrettably scarfed down a cheese-filled tortilla chip.

"When will she be back?"

"Who knows? She always leaves."

"She leaves you by yourself?"

"Why do you look so surprised? Yes, she leaves me by myself. I'm used to it. Don't worry, we'll be okay. I'll take care of us."

Sissy and I finished the rest of our Mexican entrée. I helped her unpack and stack her luggage in the corner before making a pallet on the fluffy living room carpet.

Perfume and cigarettes trailed Mama as she entered the room. She was decked out in a fancy red dress with pointy high heels. Mama was always crying broke, but had the money to shop at famous department stores for herself.

"Where are you going, Mama?"

"To see a man about a dog."

"What kind of dog?" Sissy questioned.

"A big one." Mama laughed.

"Look, I need you to watch your sister. I'm going to leave for a little while. Here's a couple of dollars, just in case." She threw the money on the counter and headed for the door without breaking her stride.

"I need to call my dad. Where's the phone?" Sissy asked me.

"We don't have one, but I'll take you over to Aunt Mary's tomorrow. You can call him from there."

I helped her get ready for bed and we lay down and talked until we feel asleep.

The next morning, we walked to the store to get cereal and milk. On our way back, I saw a group of neighborhood kids hanging in front of the building next to ours. We walked past them but didn't stop.

"Those kids look around your age. You should go say hi," Sissy said.

I wanted to, but my interactions with the G-G had deterred me from wanting to make new friends. Instead, I changed the subject and shooed Sissy into the house. Just as we got in the door, I heard a male's voice in the distance.

"Hey, girl."

I turned to find two boys walking towards us. "Sissy, go in the house. I'll be there in a minute."

"Hey," I said to the boys.

"What's your name?"

"Nikki."

"My name is Willie and this is my cousin, Mike."

"You just move in?"

"Yeah, a couple of weeks ago."

"Where from?"

"The city."

"A gritty city gal, huh?"

"No. Not really. I'm not from St. Louis."

"I didn't think so. You talk kind of proper."

Willie was cute, but not as cute as André. He didn't look as dirty and country as the city boys either.

"Can I call you sometime?"

"I don't have a phone."

"Well, can I come over?"

"I don't think so. Especially, if my mama ain't at home."

"Alright, cool. Maybe I'll see you outside, with your cute self."

Willie gave me a grin before turning and walking away. When I opened the door, Sissy was standing there with a bowl of cereal in her hands.

"He was cute," she said, with a mouth full of cereal.

"He was alright."

"It looked to me that he was more than alright the way you were smiling."

"Girl, shut up and eat your cereal so we can go over to Aunt Mary's."

On the way to Aunt Mary's, I noticed Willie and his friends were still outside. Our eyes connected, but I quickly turned my head and pretended to talk to Sissy. We made it over Aunt Mary's, but no one was home.

"Nobody's here. Let's go back to the apartment."

"But… I want to talk to my dad."

"What do you want me to do? I don't have a phone in my pocket."

"Can we wait for a little while to see if she comes home?"

"Ok, just a little while longer. Then we're going back home."

Sissy and I waited for over an hour for Aunt Mary to come home, but she never did. When I told Sissy it was time to go, her eyes filled up with tears. "But, I want to talk to my dad." I gave Sissy a hug then reached for her hand. "Come on. Maybe we can find a payphone by the corner store." Sissy's eyes lit up. She flashed a big smile and held my hand tightly.

We walked through the neighborhood and around the corner to the store. I remembered there was a payphone in front of the store. I didn't have any change, so we had to go inside.

"Nikki, I'm hungry. Can I get some chips and a soda?"

"Go ahead."

My stomach was growling, too. I'd become so accustomed to being hungry, the pain I felt in stomach was a part of my day. I wandered down the chip aisle, picked up a small bag of Sundance chips and a peach Vess soda, and then made my way to the counter. Sissy followed soon after. I paid for our treats and hurried to use the payphone.

"Do you know your number by heart?"

"Of course: 253-555-5722."

I dialed the number and handed her the phone. "Hi, Dad! Sorry it took me so long to call you. Mom doesn't have a phone. Nikki and I are at a payphone."

"Nikki, my Dad says hi."

"Tell him I said hi."

I hadn't talked to Donny in a long time. The last time I saw him, we were standing in the living room and I was asking why I couldn't stay with him and Sissy. He tried to explain, but my heart couldn't understand. I was so upset with him, I vowed to never call him Dad again and I didn't. Ever since, I called him by his first name, Donny.

Sissy carried on and on about her plane ride and how hot it was in St. Louis. It didn't take long for the conversation to shift. "Umm, I don't know where she is." I knew Donny was asking her where Mama was. I nudged Sissy, shook my head and whispered, "Tell him she's at work."

"Oh, Dad, I just remembered. She's at work. Okay, I'll tell her to call you when she gets home. Love you, too. Bye." She hung up the phone and faced me, looking perplexed. "Why did you tell me to lie to my dad about Mom?"

"Because Mama don't like people knowing her business."

"Why?"

"I don't know. She tells me to never tell her business, so I don't. Here. Eat your chips and come on."

When we got home, Mama was in the kitchen, cooking as if nothing happened. The house smelled of ground beef, onions and green peppers. All of the ingredients for Mama's meatloaf. I could hear the soft melodic voice of Sade playing in the distance. It felt like old times in Washington. Although I was happy to see Mama, I remained disappointed that she left us.

"Hey! Where have you two been?"

"I took Sissy to call Donny."

"Did you talk to him?"

Sissy replaced her words with a nodded 'yes.'

Mama stopped what she was doing and gave me and Sissy her undivided attention. "Well, go on. What did he ask you?"

"He asked about my flight and how I liked it here."

Satisfied, Mama turned and continued stirring something on the stove. "Did you tell him I went out last night?"

Sissy stood there, frozen and scared. Her eyes were big as plums. "No. I didn't say anything."

"Did he ask where I was?"

"Umm, yes, but I told him you were at work."

"Good girl. I don't like people knowing my business. I don't care who it is. Okay?"

I watched as Mama stripped Sissy of her innocence. She was no longer a sweet little girl. Mama had turned her into a liar. I could tell that Mama's request made her feel uncomfortable. She didn't say much during dinner. Afterward, she sat on the dining room area floor and listened to her Walkman.

I lay on the carpet, looked at the ceiling and imagined lying under the stars. My view was blocked by a shadowy figure standing over me.

"What's wrong with Sissy? Why is she so quiet?"

I looked over my head to find Mama standing there with her hands on her round hips.

"I don't know. I didn't do anything to her." I sat up and turned and faced her.

"Yeah, right. You did something. What did you tell her? Were you mean to her? You're always doing something."

"No, Mama, I promise. We had a good day. I took her to the store and everything."

Mama bent over and met my face with her finger drawn. "Better nothing happen to my baby while she's with you or I'm going to beat your tail."

"Okay, Mama."

All I could think about is why she didn't care what happened to me. I wondered, *Am I that invisible to her?* Since we were little, she always favored Sissy. If I did one thing wrong, she would beat the life out of me. Maybe it was because Sissy was the youngest and Donny was there to help her. Either way, Mama's disdain for me made me despise Sissy. I know it wasn't her fault, but she was easier to pick on.

* * *

Dear God,

Sissy has been here for a few days and has already taken Mama away from me. I see the way Mama looks at her and smiles, but when she looks at me, she frowns and rolls her eyes. I wish I could be more like Sissy. Would Mama love me more? I pray that things will get better soon. I'm tired of being sad all the time. I bet my dad is always happy. I can't wait to see him. Amen.

CHAPTER

Eleven

"WHAT TIME IS IT, Nikki?" Sissy tapped my shoulder.

"I don't know. Leave me alone. I'm trying to sleep!" I pulled the covers over my head.

"Nik-ki! Get up! Where is the remote?"

"Little girl, if you don't leave me alone…" I sat up and threw off the covers, hoping to find the black remote hidden somewhere under the sheets. I turned over the pillow and found it nestled in the corner of the bed. "Here!" I threw the remote to her. "Why are you making all that noise about the remote anyway?"

"My stories are getting ready to come on."

"Stories? Like, soap operas?" I laughed so hard I almost fell to the floor. "Only old ladies watch those shows."

"I'm not old and I watch the soaps."

"That's because you're weird."

"No, I'm not! And, stop calling me that before I tell Mom!"

"I don't care. Tell her! She's never here anyway."

"So... I'll tell her when she comes home," Sissy sassed.

"Whatever. That's why I'm not giving you the remote."

"Give it to me, Nikki!" Sissy got mad and balled up her fist like she was going to hit me.

"Girl, please! What are you going to do? You better get on somewhere."

"I said, give me the remote!" She pushed me and I fell off the bed and onto the floor.

"Ha-ha, that's what you get!" Sissy laughed and stuck out her tongue.

I was infuriated, "Oh, yeah? You want the remote? Here you go!" When Sissy stuck out her hand to reach for the remote, I hit her with the remote on the top of her hand as many times as I could.

"Ha-ha! It's not so funny now, is it?!"

Sissy shouted, "Ouch!" and began to cry. "I'm telling Mom on you!"

The reality of what I did set in quickly. *Oh, my God. If she tells Mama, she's going to beat me for sure.* I tried to calm Sissy down, but nothing worked.

"I'm sorry Sissy. Here, let me see it." She held her hand as if I had broken it and stuck it out for me to examine it. It was red and puffy. I became even more petrified.

I ran downstairs, got some ice and put the cubes in a towel I found on the counter. "Here's some ice. Put it on your hand." Sissy kept crying and holding her hand.

"Please stop crying. I didn't mean it. PLEASE don't tell Mama." My heart was beating so fast. I knew if she didn't calm down soon and Mama walked in, I was going to be in deep doo-doo.

"Here's the remote. You can watch whatever you want." Sissy's streaming tears decreased to a few wet spots and some panting. "Whatever I want?"

She knew she had the upper hand. I knew if Mama found out that I had hit her "baby" all hell was going to break loose.

We spent the rest of the afternoon watching *The Young and the Restless* and any other show she wanted to torture me with. Sissy also made me her slave for the day. Her excuse for not being able to do ANYTHING was, "My hand hurts." We both knew she was faking it, but I was in no position to say no.

After a long morning of waiting on Sissy hand and foot, I retreated to the front porch to get some air. I watched the kids play Double Dutch in the middle of the driveway. I could also hear MC Breed playing from the neighbor's window, "Ain't no future in yo frontin'..." I rocked back and forth to the beat and sang the lyrics to myself. I saw Willie and his friend walking to the building next to ours.

Oh, crap! I hope he didn't see me! My hair was standing up on top of my head and I was wearing a shirt decorated with food from last night's meal. I attempted to hide close to an adjacent bush, hoping somehow I would blend in. But it was too late. Willie had spotted me and started to walk over.

Damn it! I dashed for the door. Once inside, I turned

my shirt inside out and patted my hair down as best as I could. I also smelled under my arms and my breath to make sure I was fresh. I ran back outside and closed the door behind me as he made it to the doorstep.

"You didn't see me coming over here?"

"Yeah, I saw you. I had to run into the house really quick."

"For what?"

I thought if I told Willie the truth he would think that I was crazy. Therefore, I settled on a snappy comeback. "Dang, you sure are nosey."

Willie smiled slightly and moved in closer. "Maybe I just want to get to know you."

"Yeah, right. You don't look like the kind of boy that gets to know anyone." I backed away.

"Why you say that?"

"I don't know. You're a cute boy. I'm sure you've gotten to know a lot of girls."

Willie chucked and rubbed his fade. "No, not really. All these girls in the County are the same—money-hungry and stuck up. I'm looking for something different."

Willie walked forward and got close to my face as if he was looking for a kiss. With each step, I retreated backwards until I fell into the door, pushing it open and tripping into the house.

Willie poked his head in. "Dang! You weren't lying. Y'all must have just moved in. Ain't nothing in here."

Embarrassed, I attempted to rationalize with him but I couldn't find the words.

"Well…umm, yeah. My mama hasn't gotten around

to getting furniture yet. She's been busy with work." Willie pushed past me and stood in the middle of the living room, searching for a stitch of what makes a home comfortable.

"So… you at home alone?"

"Yeah… I mean, no, my little sister is here."

"Oh, yeah? If she looks anything like you, I want to meet her, too."

"Come on." I said pointing to the door. "You can't be in my house."

Willie ignored my request. "Hey, you got something to drink?"

"Come on, Willie. You have to go." I could imagine Mama coming home and finding Willie in the house. She would've beat me for sure.

"Just get me some cold water and I'll leave. I promise." Willie crossed his heart with his right pointer finger.

"Alright, but then you have to go."

"That's cool."

I hurried to the kitchen to find a cup. Willie followed me. I opened the fridge and closed it quickly so Willie couldn't see how empty it was.

"Wait a minute. Open your fridge again."

"No. Why?"

"I thought I saw something else in there."

"It doesn't matter what you thought you saw. You asked for water. Here you go." I handed Willie a red plastic cup and stood there until he finished every last drop.

"You ain't got to get snappy, girl." Willie gave me

the cup. "Can I have some more?" Willie flashed a crooked smile.

"Alright." I hesitated, but cracked the refrigerator door a little bit, hoping to grab the water pitcher without exposing our lack of food to him. Willie was so close I could feel his breath on my neck.

"Dang, back up!"

"Damn! Y'all ain't got nothing in there. You barely have enough food in there to make a nice sauce!" Willie laughed and cracked jokes for what seemed like forever.

Overwhelmed and angry, I closed the refrigerator door and tried to think of a comeback. But I couldn't. Willie was right, Mama left us with nothing. Just enough condiments to make a ghetto concoction.

"Why didn't you tell me you was poor? I could've helped you out, girl."

"I ain't poor. My mama hasn't been to the store yet."

"It look like your mama don't do much of anything around here."

"Don't be talking about my mama!" I got in his face. I was sure Willie was going to beat me up, but I wasn't going to stand there and let him talk about my mama like that.

"Or what?" he asked, peering down at me.

"You know what? I think it's time for you to go!"

"What? You mad?" Willie questioned. "I was just playing."

"No, I'm not mad, but my mama will be home soon and I don't want to get in trouble."

Again, Willie ignored my request and resorted to buttering me up. "You know I like you, right?" He cornered me in the space between the fridge and the kitchen counter. Then, he grabbed my waist, pulled me towards him and tried to kiss me.

I quickly turned my head to meet my right shoulder and expressed my discomfort. "What are you doing? You need to go." I pushed Willie off of me and hurried towards the front door.

Willie's face changed "Damn girl. Why you tripping?"

"I'm not tripping. My little sister is upstairs. Plus, my mama will be home soon."

He walked after me, grabbing my forearm when we caught up. "Come on. We'll be fast. Nobody will ever know."

I snatched my arm away. "No! I said you have to go!"

Willie smacked his lips to show his disapproval. "Yeah, whatever. You're just like the rest of them funny-acting hoes around here leading cats on. I saw how you was smiling at me and switching your butt."

"What? I wasn't switching my butt at you."

"Whatever. You should be happy a dude like me wanted to talk to you. You ain't worth my time anyway."

My feelings were hurt. "Well, bye then, lil' dude. You ain't nobody." I pushed my way past Willie, ushering him out the door and slamming it behind him.

"That's why you're dirty! You stupid bitch!" Willie yelled from outside of the door. "I bet not catch you outside. I'm going to have my sister kick your ass!" He kicked the door and walked away.

I stood in front of the door with my back glued to it, listening to Willie spouting obscenities as he walked to his destination.

"Nik-ki, is Mom back?" Sissy called from the top of the stairs.

"No. That was me closing the door."

"Who's outside yelling?"

"Nobody. It's probably the neighbors."

"Okay. Are you coming back upstairs? My hand still hurts."

I rolled my eyes and muttered to myself, "This little girl is getting on my nerves." I called out, "Yes, Sissy! I'll be up in a minute."

"Oh, and can you bring me some water when you come?"

"Yes, Sissy," I said in a monotone voice.

Before meeting Sissy's demands, I took a few deep breaths to calm myself then made my way to the kitchen to fetch Sissy's cool drink. As I climbed the steps, I replayed Willie's words, *"You ain't worth my time anyway!"* His words cut deep. The sorrow I felt consumed every part of my heart.

I'd felt that way so many times in the past. Worthless, alone—like a nobody. I was hurt that someone else could see the pain I tried so desperately to hide. Furthermore, I was upset that the one person I wanted to see it chose to ignore it.

"Here." I handed Sissy her cup of water.

"Thank you," she replied, grabbing the cup with her 'unbroken' hand. "When is Mom coming back?"

"Soon." I couldn't find it in my heart to tell Sissy that

Mama may not be back for days. She looked so sweet and innocent. From that moment, I made a promise that I would put my feelings aside and take care of Sissy like I did when we were little.

"Don't worry. I'll take care of you."

Sissy looked at me and smiled. "Thanks. That's nice."

So many things had happened since the last time I saw Sissy. I had a lot of pain in my heart, which made me bitter towards her. I didn't understand why I had to live so hard, while Sissy had it so easy. I'm sure Donny made sure she had food and clean clothes. I had to settle for choosing between washing my clothes and having food. It didn't seem fair.

* * *

Dear God,

Why me? It seems everywhere I go there's drama. Today, I had to fight off one of the neighborhood boys. Mama still isn't home and me and Sissy don't have any food. Why are you doing this to me? What did I do? Whatever it was, I'm sorry. I promise I won't do it again. Please stop the pain I feel in my heart. I can't take it anymore. Amen.

CHAPTER

Twelve

Dear God,

It's been a few days since we've seen Mama. Sissy keeps asking questions, but I don't know what to tell her. We have one more pack of soup left. I'll give that to Sissy in the morning. Also, Me and Sissy haven't washed clothes since she's been here. If Mama doesn't come tonight, I'm going to go over Aunt Mary's house, call Donny and tell him everything. What could be so important that she leaves us for so long? Please tell Mama to come home. I don't know what to do. Amen.

* * *

I PRAYED THAT NIGHT for Mama to come and get us, but she didn't. The next morning, Sissy and I shared a package of instant noodles then we got ready to go over Aunt Mary's house to call Donny.

When I opened the front door, I noticed there were more kids than usual outside. Willie was there, too. I did my best to walk by Willie without making any eye contact, but I overheard him talking to his friends as we passed by.

"Remember that girl I told you about who lives in that empty-ass apartment? There she is!"

I put my arm around Sissy and walked as fast as I could.

"Oh, you ain't going to speak?" Willie yelled from behind me. "You bum-ass bitch. I know you hear me talking to you!"

I didn't answer. I just kept on walking as fast as I could, pulling Sissy along with me.

"Isn't that the boy who came over the other day?"

"Yeah."

"Why is he being so mean to you?" Sissy looked back at Willie.

"I don't know. I guess he's mad because I wouldn't have sex with him. It's my fault. I knew I shouldn't have let him in the house."

I could tell Sissy felt sorry for me by the way she tightly held my hand. "Don't worry about him. I'm going to call my dad and tell him to come and get us."

I pleaded with God to inspire Donny to let me stay with him and Sissy, but I didn't get my hopes up. After all, he was the reason I was living in that hellhole with Mama. If he would've let me stay in Washington, my life would've been a whole lot better. I wouldn't be hungry and alone while Mama was out searching for love. The more I thought about Mama's lack of parenting skills, the more I became vexed. Mama doesn't even care enough about Sissy to stay home while she's in town.

"Do you think he'll let me come?" I asked.

"Why wouldn't he? You're his daughter, too."

I wanted to believe Donny had accepted me as his daughter, but my heart wouldn't allow it. If he loves me so much, why wouldn't he let me stay?

"Did he say that?"

"No, but I think he means to."

Sissy's response validated my feelings. *Donny doesn't care about me. All he cares about is Sissy. I bet he'll leave me here to rot, just like Mama does.* My thoughts wandered until we got to Aunt Mary's house.

When we reached Aunt Mary's, I didn't see her car. We knocked on the door and rang the bell, but no one came to the door. I feared if we went back home too soon, Willie and his friends would still be outside. Instead, I told Sissy we were going to wait for Aunt Mary, hoping to buy some time.

We waited and waited, but once again, Aunt Mary never came home. Since it had been a few hours, I felt confident Willie and his crew had gone home. To be sure, we took the long way home. With our apartment in sight, I felt as if we had victoriously eluded Willie and his friends. My thinking quickly changed when I saw Willie and his pals sitting on the steps beside our apartment.

"Damn," I said, ducking down on the side of the apartment building adjacent to ours. "How will we get by them without him seeing us?"

"Who? That boy?"

"Yes. I don't have a good feeling about this." I

remembered Willie saying if he caught me outside he was going to have his sister kick my ass.

"Do you think he's going to hit you?"

"No. I think he's going to get his sister to do more than hit me."

I tried to quickly think of a plan, but my fear was getting in the way. "Think…think… think…" I tapped the side of head next to my temple, looking for inspiration. "Okay, got it," I whispered to Sissy, "When I count to three, run as fast as you can to the house, okay?"

I waited until the coast was clear before telling Sissy to run as fast as she could to the door. "One…two…three, run!" She ran like lightning and dashed in the door, closing it behind her. I didn't want to draw attention to myself, so I decided to walk swiftly until I reached the front door.

I waited until Willie was distracted by a round booty girl in white shorts who had walked past before making my move. Like I had done so many times before, I counted to three in my head, *One…two…three…go!* My heart pounding and on the brink of tears, I walked as fast as I could to our apartment door.

I made it halfway before hearing Willie's voice. "There she is y'all! I'm going to show you how we treat stuck-up chicks around here!"

I stood there motionless as Willie and his mob gathered around me.

"You think you're too good for me, huh?"

I was petrified. All I could do was stand there and stare at Willie. *Oh, my God. Am I going to have to fight this boy? He's going to kick my ass for sure.*

Furious that I didn't respond, Willie got closer in my face to get my attention. "You hear me talking to you?"

My hands were shaking in the tightly clenched fists I had created to defend myself. "No, I don't think I'm too good for you, but you better get out of my face!"

"Or what?" Willie was standing so close to my face, I could smell the burrito he had for lunch.

"Or…it's whatever!" I rolled my neck.

I knew I couldn't beat Willie, but I was tired of being picked on. Whether the G-Gs, Mama or Willie, I couldn't take it anymore. Willie thought my reply was hilarious.

"Girl, please. You better be glad I don't hit gals. I would knock you out with one punch. You're not worth my time. I don't mess with poor girls, anyway. But, don't worry. I got someone to handle you for me."

"Let me guess. It's your sister," I sassed.

"You ain't going to be doing all that talking when she punching you in the mouth." Willie and the crowd broke out in laughter.

My eyes welled up with water, but I wouldn't allow one tear to drop. I rushed past Willie, bumping his shoulder on my way to the exit. Once I reached the end, there was a girl standing there waiting for me.

"Oh, so you're the bitch my brother told me put him out of her house?" The girl was taller and bigger than me. She had a freshly greased face to protect her skin from scratches and her medium-length hair swept into a messy ponytail. It was clear that she came to fight.

Caught off guard, I responded, "Yeah, I mean no."

I heard Sissy helplessly calling to me from the doorway. "Nik-ki! Nik-ki, come in the house!"

I was scared, but I did my best to stand my ground.

"Look. I don't know what you're talking about. I'm about to go home."

"No, you ain't!"

"Whatever!" I said, waving my hand and walking past her. That was a mistake. Once I passed her, she grabbed the back of my hair and hit me on the right side of my face.

The crowd erupted. "Fight, fight! Get her, Lesha!"

I grabbed her hand, ripped it from my hair and snatched her ponytail instead. She swung, hitting me in the face a few times. I blocked her punches as best as I could with my forearm, while holding on tight to her hair.

I felt like I had a chance to win the fight, but the thrust of our adrenaline caused me to fall into a prickly bush in front of the neighbor's apartment. I knew if Lesha got me on the ground, I was dead meat, so I fought my way out of the bush, swinging wildly and hitting her in the face.

"Nikki, please come in!" Sissy cried and called from the front of the apartment.

"Get in the house, Sissy!" I yelled, out of breath.

The scene was pure chaos. People were yelling and gathering from everywhere in the neighborhood.

My punch stunned Lesha. However, the crowd's taunts seemed to make her madder. She picked up a stick from the ground nearby and began hitting me with it.

I held up my arms to block her hits, but they hurt too much. "Ouch, you crazy bitch!" I yelled. I picked up a rock and threw it at her, hitting her in the chest. It didn't faze her.

After the last swat, I ran as fast as I could to our apartment. Sissy was waiting for me by the door. "Nikki, are you okay?" Sissy ran to the kitchen and wet the dishtowel, attempting to treat my wounds.

"Yes," I said, wiping my tears and picking the leaves and dirt out of my hair. Sissy softly patted the scratches on my arms, legs and face with the cool, damp towel.

"Who was that girl?"

"Willie's sister, Lesha."

As she tended to my wounds, I could hear people laughing and hollering outside. "Ha! You're a punk. You better run! We better not catch you outside again!"

I could hear a female yelling and banging at the door. "Come back outside, bitch! I know you can hear me."

"Let's go upstairs, Sissy." I made sure the door was locked and then went up the steps to the bathroom to check my face.

"She scratched me up pretty good," I mumbled. Next, I wiggled my fingers and checked my teeth to make sure everything was in working order. Sissy was sitting on the bed when I came out.

"I want to go home!" Tears were streaming down her cheeks.

"I don't blame you. This place isn't for little girls like you anyway." I sat next to her and placed my arm around her shoulders. "Hopefully, Mama will come home tonight and you can call Donny."

All that fighting had me tired. I peeled off my clothes and got under the covers, eventually falling asleep. I felt like I could sleep forever, but I was shaken out of my sleep by a distant voice ringing in my ears.

"Nikki, get your ass up. You're supposed to be watching Sissy. What are you doing asleep?"

I popped up to find Mama standing at the end of the bed and Sissy attached to her waist like a belt.

"I must have fell asleep."

"What happened to your face?"

I scanned my face with the tips of my fingers, feeling the scratch under my right eye. "Nothing. I fell into a bush outside." Sissy started to open her mouth, but I gave her the evil eye.

"Well, hurry up and get dressed. We're staying over my friend's house tonight." Mama took off her red jacket and laid it on the bed before heading to the bathroom.

"Sissy, don't say a word to Mama. Okay?"

"Okay," she said, looking at her dingy white socks.

I slowly got up, limited by the pain my body was causing me. After getting dressed, I packed a bag of lightly worn clothes and rushed downstairs to see if Willie and his crazy sister were still outside. I peered through the blinds, but didn't see anyone in sight. Thank God they're gone.

"Who are you looking for?" Mama questioned from behind me.

"No one."

"Girl stop playing and come on. I don't have all day."

Mama opened the door and headed to her car. Sissy followed closely behind her. I looked around before coming outside and closing the door behind me.

"What's wrong with you?" Mama snapped.

"Nothing, Mama. Just making sure I have everything."

"Well, come on!"

After confirming no one was around, I hurried to the car. Deep inside, I hoped I wouldn't have to come back to Countryside Apartments. As Mama drove off, I closed my eyes tight and asked God to take me somewhere nice, with cabinets full of food and a cushy bed to sleep in. When I opened my eyes, the Countryside sign was in the distance.

Relieved, I caressed my hands and silently ran through the events that had occurred earlier. *Where has Mama been all day?* I wondered. *Was she with her 'friend' all day?* It didn't seem like she went to work anymore. *How is she paying the rent?*

Every time she came home, she looked as though she'd been partying. It grew more evident that Mama was leaving us for the hell of it. *I've got to get away from her. If I don't, something terrible is going to happen.*

CHAPTER

Thirteen

Dear God,

Mama took us over some guy named Harry's house. He lives right up the street in the swanky Sierra Vista Apartments. His apartment is really nice. He has white furniture and awards all over the wall from AT&T. I think he's famous or something. We've been over here for two days and Sissy and me have hardly seen Mama. She stays in the room with Harry, while me and Sissy sit in the living room watching TV all day. The only good thing is Harry is nice and has a lot of food. She's so fake. I am so tired of her bull crap. I can't wait to get far away from her. Amen.

* * *

HARRY'S APARTMENT was about three blocks away

from Countryside. I was pissed, knowing Mama had been right up the street all that time while me and Sissy were left at the empty-ass apartment hungry and alone. I felt an intense amount of hate for her and I wanted her to know it. Each time she tried to talk to me, my answers were short and to the point.

"What's wrong with you, Nikki?"

"Nothing," I said, barely removing my focus from the TV screen.

"It don't look like nothing is wrong with you."

I didn't respond. The truth was I knew I was safe as long as Harry was there. She wouldn't dare show her ugly side in front of him. He was her lucky Lotto ticket.

I gestured to Sissy, clearing my throat. "Umm, Sissy didn't you say you wanted to call your dad?"

"Girl, no!" Mama snapped. "You can't be running up Harry's phone bill."

Mama locked her eyes on me and mumbled, "You better chill out before I kick your ass."

Yeah, whatever, I thought. *She ain't going to do nothing.* Although there was an overwhelming amount of insolence within me, I knew my limits. Instead of pushing the boundary, I kept my mouth closed and regrouped.

"Mama, Sissy really wants to call Donny. She hasn't spoken to him in days. Is it okay if we ask Mr. Harry if she can call long distance?" I put on my best puppy dog face, but Mama wasn't buying it.

"Oh, so you want to be sweet? What are you up to?"

"Nothing. I just want Sissy to be happy." I smiled.

I was lying through my teeth. I even pulled one of

my eyelashes so my eyes would water a little.

She was right, I was up to something. I wanted Sissy to call Donny and tell him everything. I also knew we had to be sneaky about it because Mama would do anything to protect her farce of an image.

She was quiet for a minute before responding. "I'll ask him in a little while."

"Okay, Mama," we said in unison.

She knew something was up, but she wasn't sure what.

I waited until Mama went back in the room before telling Sissy my plan. I turned to her and whispered, "Sissy, we need to get away from Mama."

"I know. I want to go home. She's barely spent any time with me since she picked me up from the airport."

"When you call Donny, tell him you want to go home and ask if I can come too, okay?"

"Okay, I will."

Sissy and I watched Saturday morning cartoons until Harry appeared in the kitchen wearing a brown fluffy robe.

"You girls alright?"

"Yes, sir."

"Sir? Darling, you can call me Harry."

"Okay, Harry."

Harry looked older than Mama, like most of the men she dated. He had a Jheri curl and wore a lot of jewelry on his fingers. The only thing I could see him and Mama having in common was her want for his money.

"Are you girls hungry?"

Sissy looked at me for approval before answering, "Yes,

Mr. Harry."

"What would you like to eat?" Harry asked, holding onto the backs of two very expensive-looking dining room chairs.

"Do you have any cereal?"

"Cereal? Honey, you can have whatever you want," Harry said, opening his arms and revealing his nappy chest hair.

Sissy and I laughed under our breath. Also, I was amused at the thought of having "anything" I wanted. I imagined asking Harry to fly me and Sissy back to Washington. Instead, I settled on the food items dearest to my taste buds.

"How about pancakes, eggs and grits?"

"You got it, young lady!" Harry pointed and opened the silver refrigerator.

Mama came into the kitchen, sporting a huge grin and silk pajama bottoms. Part of me was happy to see her smiling, but the other half knew this relationship would crash and burn like all of the others.

She acted different when she was with her "friends." She spoke softer, smiled a lot and addressed them with "Yes, baby." It was sickening. Especially since I could hardly get close to Mama without her screaming at me. Watching her be fake made me nauseous, but I hid my frustration with a slight grin and cooperation because I knew it would only be a matter of time before I was out of there.

"Mama, did you ask Mr. Harry if Sissy could use the phone to call Donny?" Mama looked vexed.

"No. Not yet, sweetheart." She tried to conceal her anger with a smile. But her balled-up top lip told another story.

But, I didn't stop. "Oh. Well, I don't think Mr. Harry will mind. He said we could have whatever we wanted." I smiled. I got up from the living room floor and walked into the kitchen. "Didn't you, Mr. Harry?"

Harry had his back turned to us, busy cooking breakfast. "I sure did young lady."

Mama was pissed. She looked at me with daggers in her eyes and whispered, hoping to keep her threats silent. "You little heffa, what are you up to? Wait until we get home." She reached and pinched my left forearm with her long red nails. She held on until Harry turned around.

"Ouch!" I said, rubbing my arm vigorously.

"Sure, I don't mind if you need to use the phone. It's alright with me."

"Thank you, Mr. Harry!"

"Darling, I told you to call me Harry. We're going to be family soon. No need for formalities."

Family soon? I thought. *I guess Mama finally found her sucker.*

"Where's the phone, Mr.…I mean, Harry?"

"There's one in the back room. Take as long as you want, sweetheart."

I wanted to jump up and down and scream at the top of my lungs. Finally, I had outsmarted Mama. Even better, I knew Sissy was her way out of St. Louis.

We hurried to find the phone to call Donny before Mama came to destroy our plan.

"The phone's just ringing," Sissy said.

"Give it a second. Maybe he's trying to get to it."

"I got the voicemail."

"Wait, hang up."

"Why?"

"Just hang up for a minute. We'll call right back."

Sissy hesitantly placed the receiver on the hook.

"What were you going to say on the message?" I quizzed her.

"I was going to tell my dad to call me."

"No, you have to do better than that!" I paced on the fluffy tan carpet.

"What do you mean?" Sissy scrunched up her eyebrows in confusion.

"Tell him what's going on and that you're ready to come home. Ask him to send someone to get us."

"Okay, I'm ready. Let's call back."

"It's ringing." The phone rang a few more times before the voicemail picked up again.

"Daddy, it's me. Can you please come and get us? Mom keeps leaving me with Nikki. I think she's a gang member."

"Sissy!"

"Well, I don't know if she's a gang member, but we don't have any food and now we're over a strange man's house with Mom. Please come and get us! Bye."

Sissy hung up the phone. "How was that?"

"A gang member, Sissy?"

"Sorry."

"Oh my God! Now he's going to think I'm a troublemaker."

"No, he won't. I'll fix it when he calls."

I was worried. What if he doesn't take me with them?

What will I do? I took three deep breaths and told myself, "Everything will be okay."

"Girls, breakfast is ready!" Harry called from the kitchen.

Sissy and I sat at the fancy glass dining table like nothing had happened. Mama continued to smile between cutting her eyes at me.

"You girls ready to throw down?" Harry placed our plates in front of us, loaded with bacon, eggs and fluffy blueberry pancakes. It smelled so good that my mouth was watering. I couldn't wait to dig in.

"First, let's bless our food. God is good. Lord, let us thank you for this food..." As Harry administered the blessing, I silently conducted a prayer of my own.

Dear God, please let Donny get Sissy's message and come and get us. I pray that he will find it in his heart to take me too, even though Sissy told him I was a gang member. I'm counting on you, God. Amen.

"Dig in, ladies!"

"So…Sissy. Did you get ahold of your father?"

"No," Sissy answered, with a mouth full of bacon. "He didn't answer. I left a message."

"Mom, when are we going home?" Sissy asked.

"Maybe tomorrow, sweetheart. Why? Are you ready to leave?" Mama wiped her mouth with one of the green cloth napkins on the table and flashed a fake half smile.

"Not really. I'm just asking. I'd rather be here than in that apartment," she said under her breath.

"What did you say?"

"Nothing, Mom."

Mama wanted to dig into Sissy, but Harry changed the subject. "Are you liking your stay in St. Louis?"

"Umm, it's okay. I miss Washington, though."

"Why is that?" Harry questioned.

"Well, St. Louis is different, that's all. Plus, at home somebody's always around."

I hoped to God that Sissy didn't say anything about Mama leaving us. Sometimes, Sissy would get ahead of herself and blab her mouth too much.

"I know y'all are over your Grandma's a lot, but I'm sure you get to see your mother pretty often, right?"

"No."

I kicked Sissy in her leg under the table and stared her down.

"Ouch! I mean yes. Grandma's house is fun, too, I guess."

I cleared my throat, distracting Harry from the truth. "Mr.... I mean, Harry. What kind of work do you do?"

"I'm a software engineer for a telecommunications company."

"What's that?"

"I make sure that people's phones are working properly."

"You must make a lot of money."

"I do okay." He chuckled. "Soon we'll all be living together in a big nice house. You won't have to worry about anything. How would you like that?"

I'm not staying here! I thought. *I'm out of here as soon as Donny sends for me and Sissy.*

We finished breakfast and for the next couple of hours, Harry and Mama kissed, laughed and talked about our fictitious future. I wanted no part of it.

By night's end, Harry and Mama headed to his room. "You girls can sleep in the guest room if you want. There's no TV, but the bed is comfortable. Good night."

"Okay. Good night, Harry."

Yes! I thought. "The phone is in the spare bedroom."

I could hear Mama in the hallway talking to Harry. "I'm going to say goodnight to the girls. I'll be right there." She came in and closed the door behind her.

"I don't know what you two are up to, but you better cut it out. Harry can make sure we're taken care of. Nikki, if you ruin my chances of getting out of the ghetto, I'll kill you." She pointed her long, fire-red fingernails in my face then slammed the door after her.

I waited for a minute before telling Sissy to call Donny back. As soon as she picked up the receiver, Mama came barreling in the door.

"Get your ass off that phone. I knew y'all was up to something." Mama snatched the phone from Sissy and unplugged it. "You ain't calling nobody else."

"But, Mom…"

"Shut up!" Mama yelled at Sissy. "I've had enough of you two. Get your asses to sleep. I'll deal with you tomorrow."

When she left, Sissy broke her silence.

"How am I going to call my dad now?"

"Don't worry. When he gets your message, he'll come and get us."

"I sure hope so."

Sissy changed into her nightclothes and climbed into

the full-sized bed. I climbed into the bed shortly after her.

* * *

Dear God,

I hate Mama. I would ask you to take her from this Earth, but I know Sissy would be sad. I can't believe Mama has been lying, saying we're over Grandma's house. What's wrong with her? I pray that Donny sends for Sissy and me so I can leave this horrible place. I hate it here. Please God, I'm begging you. Thank you, Nikki

CHAPTER

Fourteen

"SISSY – NIKKI – GET UP!" My eyes could hardly focus on the image of Mama standing over me.

"Huh?" I replied. "What time is it?"

"Girl, get your ass up! We're leaving!"

Mama seemed to be mad about something. I could tell by the way she was ripping through Harry's apartment looking for her things. Harry was standing in the hallway, watching and trying to reason with her.

"Now, Clarene, calm down. I just think we should slow things down for a little while, so I can get to know your girls."

"Get to know them? What does that mean?" Mama didn't stop stuffing her clothes into her black-and-pink duffel bag. "You said you wanted to meet them, so I brought them over. Now, all of a sudden, you don't want anything to do with me? I knew I should've left them home."

"Left them home?" Harry looked confused. "I thought they were over your mother's house?"

Mama got quiet then responded, "What I do with my kids is none of your damn business!"

The sound of Mama's voice echoed through Harry's apartment. I gave Sissy a shake, startling her out of sleep.

"Hurry up and get dressed." Sissy sat up in the bed and rubbed her eyes.

"What's wrong?"

"Mama and Harry are arguing." I could hear the muffled sound of Mama and Harry fussing and someone slamming things in his bedroom.

"About what?"

"I don't know, but something is telling me things are about to get nasty."

While we finished getting dressed and stuffing our rags into the white grocery bag that accompanied us to Harry's house, they continued to argue. Well, actually, Harry followed Mama while she walked around the house ranting and raving. Finally, Harry had enough. He grabbed Mama's duffel bag and headed towards the door.

"You know what? If you want to leave, then leave!"

Harry threw Mama's bag in front of the door.

"It's too early in the morning to be screaming and arguing with you! If this is how you're acting now, I'm glad I'm leaving your crazy ass alone."

Mama stopped dead in her tracks, threw her pocketbook on the floor and rushed towards Harry. "What did you say, nigga?" Her face was red and her eyes were full of water. It was evident that Harry had hurt her feelings.

Harry took a step back. "Woman, you better get out of my face!"

Despite Harry's warning, Mama didn't back down. She followed up by pointing her right pointer finger at his dark, wide nose. "You know what? I don't need you. I was doing your old ass a favor by being with you. It's your loss! Good luck finding somebody better. Nikki and Sissy, come on!" Mama stormed out of the door. Sissy and I ran after her. As we passed Harry, his face grew softer. I think he felt sorry for us.

Harry went and stood in the doorway. "Clarene!" he bellowed.

"Go to hell!" she screamed, struggling to get the car door open.

"You want to know the real reason I don't want to be with you?"

Mama stopped and faced Harry. Harry moved closer to her. "You're a shitty mother. You don't care about nobody but yourself. What kind of woman leaves her children for days and doesn't call one time to check on them? Look at your children. They look like they haven't bathed in days. Any man would be out of his mind to deal with you."

I was stunned. Harry wasn't that dumb after all. Mama stood in silence, staring at Harry. After a few seconds, she turned and walked to the car and called to us. "Nikki and Sissy, bring your asses out before I leave you!"

"Wait a minute, girls." He dug in his pocket and

handed us two crisp $20 bills. "Take care of each other, okay?"

I quickly took the money and stuffed it in my pocket. "Thank you, Mr. Harry."

"Nikki! What is taking so damn long? Hurry up and get y'all asses in this car before I make you walk home!"

Me and Sissy jumped in the car as Mama sped off, cursing and holding a cigarette in her left hand.

"I don't know who he thinks he is. If he can't accept you two, then I don't need him no way." Mama went on fussing and taking a drag of her cigarette in between. I didn't say a word. I just looked out the window and prayed that she didn't direct her rage towards me.

"Did you say anything to Harry? You know how you can get."

"No, Mama. I didn't say anything to him." I looked straight ahead and tried my best to speak soft and avoid eye contact. She was volatile. When she was like that, any word or look could set her off.

"I bet your stank-ass attitude turned him off. Do you know how hard it is to find a good man who will accept older children? All you had to do was smile and be nice, but you couldn't do that, huh?"

"I didn't do anything, Mama. Why are you mad at me?"

"Nikki, you're always doing something. You're always complaining about something. I'm tired of seeing your face, you make me sick!"

Sissy tried to jump to my defense. "Mom, Nikki didn't do anything! Please don't be mad at her."

"Shut up, Sissy. I'm not talking to you!"

I wanted to cry, but I was full of anger. I knew I

didn't do anything, but somehow I was still to blame. Each and every time one of her boyfriends dumped her, she took it out on me. I was tired of her abuse.

God, please let Donny come and get us today! I silently begged, while Mama continued to scold me. I was relieved to see the Countryside sign in the distance. I knew I had a better chance of getting away from Mama's punches outside of the car.

Once we pulled in, Mama shouted, "Both of you get out of my car!" I got out in a hurry, slamming the door behind me.

"Don't slam my damn door! Hurry up and get your asses in the house!" She was shouting in front of the neighborhood.

I knew the moment I walked in the door, Mama would come after me. I was so nervous that my hands were shaking and I felt like I was going to throw up.

I couldn't get in the door all the way before she approached me with her finger in tow.

"Who do you think you are, little girl?"

"Mama, why are you so mad at me? I didn't do anything," I repeated, flinching at her every move.

"What? Don't talk back to me!" Mama followed her sentence with a slap to my face. "You ain't worth shit. Who's gonna want you? Hell, I don't even want you."

Tears rolled down my cheeks and through my fingers as I held my face. But, instead of allowing her feeble remarks to break me down, I found the courage to bark back.

"That's fine! I don't want to live with you anymore. I hate it here. I want to go back to Washington."

Mama laughed and taunted me. "Yeah right, who's

going to take your simple-minded self?"

"Donny. We told him everything. How you leave us with no food while you go and hang out with different men. He's on his way to get us."

"You little bitch! I knew you were up to something!" Mama lunged for me, grabbed my shirt and commenced to beat me in the face and head. Each blow to my head made me dizzy, eventually causing me to fall against the living room wall. I did my best to cover my face and head, but she kept on hitting me.

"Mom! Please stop!" Sissy pleaded with her, but she kept on hitting me until she was too tired to continue.

Out of breath, she found haven on the wall nearest the stairs. "Don't you ever talk back to me again, you hear me? Next time, I'm going to beat your ass into a coma." After she caught her breath, Mama made her way up the stairs.

Sissy ran over to me, crying. "Nikki, are you okay?" She tried to comfort me by rubbing my wounds, but I pushed her hand away.

"It's okay. I'm fine." The truth was I wasn't okay. My head was pounding so loud I could hardly hear myself think. The pain was agonizing. Tears fell from my eyes like raindrops, causing the blood from my nose to ease into my mouth.

"Nikki, your nose is bleeding." I balled up the bottom corner of my t-shirt and wiped the blood from my nose.

"Why did she hit you like that? I want to go home, Nikki." Sissy and I hugged and cried until we heard Mama coming down the stairs. I held my breath, hoping she wasn't coming back for more.

"Nikki, watch Sissy. I'm going out." Before I had a chance to respond, she left out the door.

"She's leaving again?" Sissy questioned.

"Yes, and we have to get to a phone and call Grandma. Maybe she can come and get us until Donny gets here."

Dizzy, I got up and looked out the window to make sure Mama was gone. I didn't see her car, so I told Sissy to grab a change of clothes and we headed out the door to find a phone.

"You still have blood on your face, Nikki."

"Where?"

"Under your nose and on your cheek."

I wiped the remaining blood from my face with my sleeve and folded it so no one could see. Once we got to the phone booth, I quickly dialed Grandma's number but no one answered. Fearful that Mama would catch us, I dialed again.

"Come on. Somebody pick up!"

"Hello?"

"Grandma?"

"Yeah, who is this?"

"It's Nikki."

"Hey, Nikki Pooh. Is everything alright?"

"Can me and Sissy come over?"

"Sissy's in town?"

"Yes. Can we come over?"

"Yeah, baby. Come on.

I couldn't fathom telling Grandma that Mama had beaten me up. *What if she tells Mama and she beats me some more?* She seemed so happy to see Sissy. But I knew when she saw my face, she would know something happened.

It took us two hours to catch the bus from the County to the Northside of the city. We finally made it to the bus stop on the corner of West Florissant and Goodfella Avenue. Next we had to walk 10 blocks to get to Grandma's street. Sissy was tired, but I was excited to see Grandma and Meechie sitting at the kitchen table. Grandma greeted me and Sissy with a big smile and open arms.

"Oh, my goodness! Look at how tall you are, Sissy. How did y'all get here?"

"We took the bus," I responded, holding my head down to try to conceal my face.

"All the way from the County? Where's your mama?"

"I don't know."

"What's wrong, Nikki? Come here so I can see you."

As I walked closer to Grandma, I could feel the sorrow inside of me. I was so angry and broken, yet I had no idea how to express it. Although I did my best to hold back my tears, my pain won. Once I reached Grandma, I fell into her arms and wept.

"Grandma, I don't want to live here anymore. I want to go back to Washington."

"Whoa, whoa, whoa! What's going on?" Grandma gently tilted my head up, revealing the cuts on my face. "Baby, what happened to you?"

"My mama doesn't love me. All she does is cuss me out, leave me and beat me up. I can't take it anymore."

I could see the disappointment in her face. "What happened over there?"

I wanted to tell her, but I avoided the details of what Mama did. I guess in some way I was ashamed that I had allowed Mama's incompetence to go that far. In other ways, I wanted to spare Grandma the embarrassment that her child had grown to be a horrible mother. I knew Grandma would feel responsible. Instead, I pleaded for Grandma to grant us refuge. "Grandma, can we please stay here until Donny comes and gets us?"

Grandma looked perplexed. "Donny's coming to get you?"

"Yes, please let us stay. I can't go back to Mama's." Out of fear that Grandma would say no, I prepared myself to drop to the grey kitchen floor and tightly wrap my arms around her bottom half. She would have to pry my fingers from her legs—I would rather die than go back and live with Mama.

"Of course you can stay here, baby." Grandma put her arm around my shoulders until it reached the other side and pulled me in tight. "Go ahead and get cleaned up. Let me worry about your mama."

I slowly made my way to the bathroom, leaving a trail of tears for Meechie to follow. She came in the bathroom and closed the door behind her. "Girl, what happened?"

"It was bad at Countryside. My mama was never home. I was hungry all the time. She never bought groceries or left me money. When Sissy came, I thought things would get better, but they didn't. Then, I met a boy who turned on me because I kicked him out of our apartment. He got mad and got his sister to push me in the sticker bushes and scratch up my face. THEN, my

Mama beat me up because she said I was ruining her life." I plopped down on the cream-colored toilet seat and rested my head in my hands.

"Damn, all that happened in two months?" Meechie laughed then tried to conceal her humor. "I'm sorry for laughing, cuz, but it's just that you look so miserable." She reached over and picked a leaf out of my mangled mane and threw it in the blue wastebasket next to the toilet. "And, tore up. So… Do you think Aunt Clarene knows you're here?"

"I don't think so. I didn't leave the apartment until I knew she was gone."

"Oh, shit! You know she 'bout to come over here trippin', right? What you going to do?"

I got up from the commode and turned on the water in the sink to wash the dirt and blood from my face. Then I washed my hands and walked out of the bathroom with Meechie hot on my trail.

"Umm… You didn't answer my question."

I stopped before getting in earshot of Grandma. "I don't know yet. Hopefully, Donny comes and gets us before Mama notices we're gone. It's not like she cares about us anyway."

"Y'all going back to Washington?" Meechie's tone got softer.

"Yes, I can't stand it here. I want to find my daddy and go live with him." I turned to walk away, but Meechie grabbed my arm, urging me to stay. "Wait a minute. If y'all go…I want to go, too.

CHAPTER

Fifteen

I COULDN'T SLEEP at all that night. I kept having visions of Mama busting down the door and dragging me out of the bed. The longer I tried to stay in the bed, the louder my thoughts became. Eventually, I couldn't take it anymore. I had to get up. My feet hit the cold concrete basement floor and I scurried up the stairs to the kitchen. The house was dark except for the dim yellow light Grandma kept on over the stove.

As I moved silently through the dining room and opened the front door, a voice surprised me from the darkness. "Where you going?"

"Ahhhh!" I grabbed my chest. "Meechie, you scared the mess out of me."

"You shouldn't be trying to sneak out of the house."

"I'm not sneaking out. I'm going outside for a little while. I can't sleep."

Meechie followed me outside, wrapped in her favorite holey housecoat, and we sat on the front porch.

"What's wrong with you?

"I can't sleep."

"Why?"

"I don't know. I think I'm anxious about leaving."

"Did y'all ever talk to Donny?"

"No. Sissy tried to call again, but she said there was no answer. She left another message."

"Do you really think he's coming?"

"I think so. In my heart I feel like he's on his way."

"What you going to do if he says you can't go?"

"I'm going to run away and find my daddy. I can't stay with my Mama anymore. She's too evil.

"What happened while I was gone? Why do you want to go?" I asked Meechie.

"My mama is never home and when she is, she high or stealing from somebody in the house. It's embarrassing. The money I get from my daddy is all I have, but every chance she gets she's asking to borrow money from me or taking it. Plus, I'm tired of being in this house. I want to see something new."

"Do you think your mama will let you go?" I questioned.

"Man, she don't care about nothing but getting high. She probably won't even know I'm gone." Meechie said, wrapping herself tighter in her tattered robe.

Meechie was right. Time and time again, Aunt TeeTee had shown us how important crack was to her. Sissy told me the last time she came to visit, TeeTee left her in the car in the hot sun for hours while she smoked crack with her friends. Luckily, a man came out of the house and saw Sissy passed out in the car. Sissy said the man cursed Aunt TeeTee out something terrible before taking her to the store to buy whatever she wanted and then dropped her off at Grandma's house.

"What about Erin?"

"She'll be alright. Grandma will make sure she's taken care of."

I paused. "Hey, do you remember that time you, Grandma, and Auntie TeeTee came to Washington to visit? We had so much fun that summer."

"Yeah, I remember." Meechie smiled. "That's the year Erin fell off the handlebars of my bike and her butt got rubber-burned on the front wheel." Meechie busted into laughter.

"Shhh, stupid! You're going to wake up the neighbors!" I reminded her.

"Remember when that boy beat you up with that bat for dragging his sister out of their house by her hair? Now, that was funny!" Meechie laughed.

"No it wasn't, dummy! You just stood there and let him do it." I chuckled anyway.

"Shoot, I thought you had it. You was winning until he pulled that bat out."

"That wasn't funny, Meechie!" I laughed.

"Nah, it wasn't funny to you." She laughed so hard she tipped over and hit her head on the black iron railing.

"That's what you get!" I scolded and laughed some more.

Meechie and I reminisced and laughed as the sun rose over the harsh streets of St. Louis. It felt good to clown around with Meechie. I missed her while I was away. I hadn't laughed that much in a long time.

Between my laughs, I felt the need to cry, but I held it in. My young heart was full of worry and discontentment. I wanted to run from it, but couldn't. The scratches on my face and the bruises on my body reminded me of the torment I'd experienced since being in St. Louis.

Dear God, I silently prayed. *Please take the pain away. If you won't, I promise I will.*

"Nikki."

"Huh?"

"Did you hear anything I said?" Meechie fussed.

"Sorry, I zoned out for a minute. What did you say?"

"Never mind." She got up and walked towards the door. "Let's go in the house. I'm cold."

We went in and found Grandma sitting at the table, drinking coffee. "Hey, Grandma."

"Hey, where are you two coming from?"

"The front porch," we said in unison.

"This early in the morning?"

"Yep."

Grandma chuckled and shook her head. "Leave it to you two."

I smiled and headed to the fridge to get a glass of water.

"Listen. I talked to your mama last night."

My racing heart caused my hands to shake. I almost dropped my drink. I took a few deep breaths to calm my nerves and pulled the chair out next to Grandma. "Oh, yeah? What did she want?"

"She was worried about you, Nikki Pooh. She wants to come over later and talk to you and your sister."

I almost choked on my water. "About what?"

"I'm not sure, baby. I guess about her behavior towards you. Nikki Pooh, give her a chance. If you still want to leave, I'll help you the best that I can."

I wanted to believe Mama had turned a new leaf, but I knew better. I'd given her too many chances already. I was tired of her excuses and I wasn't going to let her trick me into staying.

"I'll listen to what she has to say, but I don't have much to say to her. I'm not staying here with her. She's too evil and I'm tired of her leaving me."

"I understand that, sweetheart. All I ask is that you give her a chance. She might surprise you."

The phone rang startling Grandma. "Who in the world is calling at this time of the morning? Nikki get the phone."

I dashed to the phone, hoping and praying it was Donny. "Hello?" I asked, mildly out of breath.

"Who is this?" The voice sounded familiar, but I couldn't quite get a handle on it.

"This is Nikki. Who is this?"

"Oh. Hey, Nikki. This is Steph. Is Aunt Rose there?"

"Yeah, hold on a minute."

I could hardly contain my happiness. If Steph was calling, it meant Donny got our messages. Steph is Mama's first cousin—the daughter of Aunt Mary and Donny. I don't know what went down between Mama and Donny, but I overheard Aunt TeeTee talking about how triflin' Mama was for sleeping with her aunt's husband. Aunt TeeTee said Donny was married to Aunt Mary for a long time, but when Aunt Mary invited Mama to Washington, Mama slept with Donny behind

Aunt Mary's back. He divorced Aunt Mary and him and Mama were together. Since that time, Aunt Mary and Mama haven't gotten along.

For those reasons, I believe Steph carried a secret resentment towards me and Sissy. Although she's always been present in our lives, she made damn sure that people didn't mistake us for her sisters. She also made it known that Donny was "her" daddy.

I wanted to trust that Steph would rescue us, but visions of her slamming the door in my face when I was eight continued to dance in my head. I could also remember Steph taking her kids to the McDonald's while me and Sissy were in the car and not buying us anything. In those days, it seemed that Steph went out of her way to be mean to us, but I felt I had no choice but to give her a chance. She was my only way out of St. Louis.

Maybe she's different now. I quietly reconciled with myself. I swiftly handed Grandma the phone and plopped down next to her to get an earful of their conversation.

"Hey, Steph! How are you? Yeah, she's okay. I think she's still sleeping in the other room. Uh-huh…uh-huh…uh-huh." I moved in closer, hoping I could catch a word or two of Steph's questions. Grandma gave me that look that meant cut it out. I adhered to her request and sat back in the chair.

"I'm not sure what happened. Her and Nikki showed up yesterday and asked to stay. So, when will you be here? Okay. Well, call me when you get in town. I love you, too. Bye."

My heart was beating fast, causing my hands to

sweat. I could barely wait for Grandma to hang up the receiver. "What did she say?" Meechie and me were glued to her every move.

"She said her and Carlos are on their way here. They were already on their way to Mississippi when Donny called and asked them to stop and get Sissy on their way."

"She didn't say anything about me?"

"No, baby. She just said they'll be here sometime tonight. Don't worry. Everything will work out, okay?"

"Alright, Grandma." I fought back my tears as I exited the kitchen and searched for a quiet place to be with my thoughts. *If Steph leaves me here, what am I going to do? Mama doesn't want me. Besides, I can't spend another day alone in that apartment.* I felt desperate and hollow. *Mama was right. No one wants me.*

As my mind wandered, my body carried me to the side of the house, where I sat in the grass and sobbed. Unfortunately, I couldn't find peace there either. Memories of Mama chasing me outside and beating me with a straw broom lived there. My heart ached, but I became determined to end the pain that day—for good. Eventually, my sorrow turned into rage then transitioned into ambition.

"Regardless of what Steph says, I'm leaving today. If she doesn't take me I'm running away." My mind was made up. I went into the house and packed the residue of my young life into my backpack and waited for Steph and Carlos to come. The house was busy with people coming in and out, but I saw nothing but blurs and heard nothing but chatters in the distance. I was lost in my thoughts and the disappointment that accompanied them.

Meechie passed through and sat next to me on the couch. "Why you looking like that?"

"Like what?" I didn't break my gaze.

"All crazy and stuff."

"I'm not. I'm waiting to see what Steph is going to say."

"Yeah, I was thinking about that, too." Meechie sat back on the couch. "What if she doesn't take us?"

I turned and faced Meechie, revealing my determination. "It doesn't matter. I'm leaving anyway."

"Girl, you sound crazy. Where are you going to go?"

"I'm going to find my daddy."

"Okay. I thought you didn't know where he is?"

"I don't, but I know his family lives in Alton. I'll go there first. Better yet, I'm going to call them."

Meechie let out a sigh and rolled her eyes. "How you going to do that if you don't know the number?"

"I'll just call 411."

"And then what?"

"Then, I'll ask where he is."

"Why can't you just wait? I have a good feeling she will take us."

"And what if she doesn't, Meechie?" I could no longer contain my anger. "I'm tired of sitting around waiting for someone to show pity on me. I'm tired of being passed around. Wake up, Meechie! Nobody wants us. Our mamas don't care about us. We're practically orphans. How is this any different than being on the streets?"

I could tell my words hurt Meechie. Her eyes welled

up with tears and her face changed in a way I'd never seen before.

"Speak for yourself! My mama loves me. She's just going through a rough time right now. One day she'll stop using drugs and everything will be like it used to be."

Meechie got up and ran into the bathroom and closed the door behind her. I followed and found her sitting on the toilet, crying.

"What do you want?" she said between tears.

"I'm sorry, Meechie. You're right. I should be more patient. I guess I should find out for sure before leaving." Deep down, she knew I was telling the truth, but just like I did, she hoped one day things would be better. Unfortunately, this was a dream I no longer carried.

I wanted out of there. It didn't matter with who, or how I would get there. I told myself I would make a way. Although I was young, I was still a realist. I knew I didn't have any money, so I prepared my mind, body and spirit for the unthinkable things I would have to endure to meet my goal. I prayed for solace, but the pain in my heart still remained.

Despite what I told Meechie about waiting, I still felt the immense desire to find my father. I waited until Meechie went in her room and Sissy and Erin were done running and playing in the living room to dial 411.

"City and state, please," spoke a monotone voice on the line.

"Umm… Alton, Illinois."

"What's your listing?"

"Listing? What is that?"

"Who are you looking for, ma'am?"

I paused. I couldn't remember the last name Mama told me, but I knew his first name.

"Andrew…"

"Ma'am, I have 1700 listings with the first name Andrew."

Just then, the name came to me. "Mason. Andrew Mason."

"I don't have an Andrew Mason, but I have a Frederick and Mary Mason."

"Okay, give me that number."

"Hold for your listing, ma'am."

An automated voice took over the call. "Here is your listing: 618-555-9845."

I wrote down the number and hung up the phone. I'd finally got a clue to the whereabouts of my daddy. A million thoughts filled my head. *Are Frederick and Mary my grandparents*? *What if this is the wrong number?* I couldn't take my eyes off the piece of paper with my handwriting on it. *What if he doesn't want to talk to me*?

I sat on the couch and pondered my decision to call. Once I found the courage, I picked up the phone, dialed the number and waited anxiously for someone to pick up.

"Hello," a mature-sounding woman said on the other end of the line.

"Hello." I echoed "Grandma?"

"Yes. Who is this?" she questioned.

"This is Nikki."

"Oh. Hey, Nikki. I was wondering when you were going call. I talked to your father the other day."

Wow. She was waiting on me to call? She knows where

my dad is? I wondered happily.

"Really?"

"Of course. When are you coming down from Chicago?"

"Chicago? I don't live in Chicago. I live in St. Louis."

"St. Louis? Did you move?"

"Yes, last year from Washington."

"Washington?" She paused. "Who is this again?"

"Nikki. Andrew's daughter."

"Andrew's daughter? Oh, I thought you were my eldest son's daughter. Her name is Nikki, too."

My heart sank. I thought she knew me, but it was all a mistake. "Is my daddy there?"

"Sweetheart, I haven't spoken to Andrew in months. The last I heard he was in California."

"California? Do you know where?"

"Yes. Wait a minute. Let me look in my address book." She put me on a brief hold and came back to the phone. "The last address I have is in Bellflower, California. Wait, I have a number too—562-555-6241. I don't know if it will work, but it's worth a try."

"Okay. Thank you."

"Bye-bye, sweetheart." She hung up the phone.

I smiled and hung up the receiver. *I found my daddy. I wonder if the number works.* Taking a chance, I dialed the number, but couldn't get out because Grandma had a long-distance block on her phone. *Damn,* I thought. *How am I going to call him now? At least, I know where he is. If Steph doesn't take me, I'll have to run away to California and find him.*

* * *

Dear God,

Please forgive me for being mean to Meechie. I didn't mean to hurt her feelings. I'm sure you know Steph is on her way. I don't think she's going to take me and Meechie with her. So, I'm going to run away. I called and talked to my grandma today. She sounds nice. She also told me where my daddy is. If Steph doesn't take me, I am going to leave tonight when Grandma goes to sleep and hitchhike to California to find my daddy. God, please send me money and protect me while I find him. I know it's dangerous, but I can't stay here anymore. Amen.

CHAPTER

Sixteen

"NIKKI, STEPH JUST CALLED and said she's ten minutes away. Get your stuff together!" Sissy yelled as she ran past me.

"Finally," I mumbled.

She returned with her bags and jacket in tow. "Are we going to say bye to Mom?"

"I don't know." I was short with Sissy; mad that Steph and Carlos were driving cross-country to rescue her without any mention of me.

"Are you mad at me?"

"No."

"Well, why are you acting like that?"

"I'm not mad, Sissy." I got up and brushed by Sissy, bumping her shoulder on my way.

Full of anxiety I could no longer sit. I paced back and forth, looking for them out of the large-paned kitchen windows.

"Girl, sit down. You're making me nervous," Grandma fussed, sitting at the front table.

"I can't. What if they don't take me?"

"You let me worry about that." She barely looked up from doing her crossword puzzle.

"They're here!" I watched from the window as Sissy ran to the car and into Steph's arms. I was excited too, but I could only think the worst.

"Hey, y'all!" Steph said, as she entered the house.

"Give me a hug. I haven't seen you in so long!" Grandma sprang out of her chair and hugged Steph tight.

Steph had put on a few pounds since I'd seen her last. Her round hips made her look mature. The weight looked good on her, but I could tell she was uncomfortable by the way she kept tugging at the fabric around her mid-section.

"You look good, Steph," Grandma said as she looked her over.

"Hey, everyone," Carlos announced as he entered the room.

Carlos was a dark-skinned, slender, mildly attractive man. He and Steph had been married for a few years. He spoke with a thick Mississippi drawl. Although he was from the South, he'd been living in Tacoma for a while. The Army had stationed him there and that's where he and Steph met.

"Hey, Nikki!" Steph called. "Come here and give me a hug." Reluctantly, I made my way to her opened arms. As we embraced, I silently spoke to her heart, asking her to take me too.

"I haven't seen you in so long. Look how tall and beautiful you've gotten."

I didn't exchange words with Steph. I just smiled, hoping it would hide the fear and resentment I was feeling.

"Have a seat. I'm sure y'all are tired." Grandma pointed to the chairs spread out around the round glass table.

Steph and Carlos grabbed a seat and melted into the chairs. "Yeah, it's been a long trip," Carlos confirmed.

"Where are the kids?"

"Oh, they're staying with my daddy until we get back."

The bags under Steph's eyes told the story of being up all night driving. Her full lips were slightly dry and her shoulder-length locks were frizzy.

"Can I get you all something to drink?" Grandma questioned.

"Yes," Steph responded.

As they made small talk, I grew impatient. I wanted to know if I could go or not. I wanted to speak up, but I didn't want to be rude. Instead, I excused myself from the table to look for Meechie. I found her in her room, hesitantly packing a small brown bag.

"Steph's here."

"I know. I heard her come in."

"Why didn't you come and say hi to her?"

"I don't know. I guess I'm nervous. I'm coming."

What Meechie didn't know was I needed her there. She always made me feel stronger. At least, if Steph said no, I would have Meechie there to lift my spirits.

On my way back to the kitchen, I overheard Grandma and Steph talking. I didn't interrupt, just stood there and listened.

"...Yeah. We're going to stay with Uncle Robert tonight and get back on the road tomorrow."

"Oh, okay. Does he still live in University City?"

"Yep. In the same house," Steph responded.

"That's nice. How is his wife doing?"

"She's good."

Grandma was silent for a moment. I could tell she was thinking about her next words. "You know Nikki's having a hard time here, right? She doesn't think I know, but Meechie told me Clarene has been leaving her to fend for herself for days at a time."

"What! Why?" Steph's voice rose a few octaves.

"I'm not sure. I think she's back to drinking."

"That's a damn shame." Steph looked at Carlos and shook her head.

"She really wants to go back with you all. What do you think about that?"

Steph paused. "Auntie, I want to, but I'm not sure. Our place is small, plus we have the kids."

"I'm sure you can make room for her, Steph. She needs somebody to take care of her. That child has been wearing the same clothes since the last time I saw her. I want to help, but you know how Clarene is...she'll take her away from me. I've been giving her money here and there, but it's not enough. She needs somebody to look after her."

"Okay." Steph looked down at the table. "We'll talk about it and let you know before we leave."

Let her know before they leave? I knew it! They ain't going to take me. My knees grew weaker the more I stood there. I gained my balance and hoped Steph would change her mind.

Their conversation was interrupted by a loud banging on the front door. "Who in the world is that?" Grandma looked towards the door.

A voice that sounded like Mama's was ranting from the other side of the door and fighting with the door handle. "Let me in. I know y'all hear me knocking!"

Carlos and Steph stood, while Grandma walked towards the door. Grandma spotted me standing in the shadows and ordered me to go to the bedroom. I heard the door open then Mama's voice cursing and yelling. I stood in the hallway and peeked in the living room, waiting to catch a glimpse of Mama's dysfunction.

"Where are my kids?"

"Clarene, you ain't 'bout to be coming in my house with all that noise. You can leave!" Grandma pointed at the door.

"I ain't going no damn where!" Mama ripped through the door, bumping Grandma on her way to the kitchen.

"Look at you. You're drunk. You need to calm down."

Mama's rants drew me closer to the kitchen, where she stood with the assistance of the wall.

"Hell naw! I ain't going to calm down. This heffa is trying to steal my kids! Who do you think you are?" She glared at Steph.

Steph and Carlos tried to talk to Mama, but she continued to scream and curse at them. "Clarene, you are in no condition to take care of those girls right now.

Let us take Nikki for a while until you get yourself together."

"Bitch, stop acting like you know me! You don't know me!" Mama jumped across the table, launching at Steph, but her drunkenness caused her to fall to the floor.

Grandma began to cry and attempted to reason with Mama. "Clarene, you need some help. Please sit down and listen."

Carlos helped Mama up from the grey-and-white tiled floor.

"Get your goddamn hands off of me!"

Her contempt continued as she pulled herself from the floor and onto a nearby chair. Her black sheer stockings had a hole and run on the knee from where she'd fallen. "This is all her fault! If that little heffa didn't call, you wouldn't be taking my kids away." Mama pounded on the table with her fist with each sentence.

"Who are you talking about, Nikki?" Grandma asked.

"Yeah, Nikki. She's always making trouble. I can't stand her ass!"

"Clarene, that's your daughter!" Steph reminded her.

"So what! Get her away from me. She's ruining my life. I should've gotten an abortion instead of letting you talk me into keeping her." Mama directed her attention to Grandma. "She's been nothing but trouble ever since she dropped out of my coochie. I can't believe I let that no-good nigga leave me alone with that bastard."

"Clarene! Shut your mouth right now!" Grandma

ordered.

Her words stung. The reality of my greatest fear had slapped me in the face. Mama never wanted me. Deep down I knew there was a reason she treated me badly, but I never truly believed she hated me.

Mama and Grandma argued back and forth until I could no longer take it. I entered the room to find Mama sitting at the kitchen table with makeup running down her face.

"Oh, baby. How long have you been standing there?" Grandma asked with tears in her eyes.

"Long enough. I heard everything she said." Grandma got up and tried to hug me, but I pushed past her and stopped in front of Mama.

"What you gotta say to me, little girl?" she asked with a smirk on her face.

"I don't want to live with you anymore. You're a rotten mother. You're always leaving and treating me like you don't love me. I heard you say you wish you would've killed me…" I could hardly get the rest of my words out. My lip trembled and tears ran uncontrollably down my face at the very thought of the horrible words she had uttered. "I wish you would've killed me too. All you ever do is tell me how much you hate me and treat me like dirt. It's not my fault my daddy left you."

My words got Mama's attention. "Little girl, who in the hell do you think you're talking to?" Mama rose from the table, knocking over the salt and pepper shakers on her way.

"Wait a minute, Clarene. Hear her out." Steph jumped between us.

"Mama, what did I ever do to you? Why don't you love me?"

Tears filled Mama's eyes. "Love you?" she laughed and sat down in her seat. "Who are you to love? You ain't nobody."

"Clarene! That is enough!" Grandma shouted.

"Like I said, take her. I don't care. She ain't going to be shit anyway. Watch." She looked me up and down. "You going to be just like me—miserable and lonely." Mama laughed and reached into her purse and pulled out a cigarette.

"You may not think so, but I have a chance if I get away from you." I retorted. Mama stood up once again, walking in my face. She was so close I could smell the liquor and cigarettes on her breath. My heart raced as I prepared for the worst.

"You ain't going to be nothing. You know why? Because you come from me. Mark my words. This world is going to chew you up and spit you out. You think you're special, but they'll use you and leave you just like they did me. If you want to leave, leave. I don't need you anyway."

Mama busted through Steph and headed towards the door, but then she came back—This time for Grandma.

"And you..." Mama pointed in Grandma's face. "This is all your fault."

"Clarene, you're drunk. You need to lie down." Grandma swatted her hand from her face.

"All of y'all think she's so perfect, but she ain't." Mama opened her arms and yelled so loud the whole house shook. "Did you tell them how you left me, Momma?"

"Clarene…g'on somewhere with that." Grandma slowly made her way to her feet.

I could see Meechie, Erin and Sissy standing at the entrance to the kitchen. Meechie spoke up. "Aunt Clarene, please…" Before Meechie could finish her sentence, Mama continued her rant.

"How dare you judge me, when you weren't there yourself!"

"You better shut your mouth," Grandma said with a demanding whisper.

"No! You shut up and listen to me!" Mama shouted.

"You left me and Michael in that foster home to be beaten and molested." She pointed her finger in Grandma's direction. "There was no one there to protect us. And where were you? Out getting drunk and looking for your next husband."

Grandma stared at her with tears running down her face, but didn't say a word. I couldn't believe what I was hearing. Steph and Carlos looked on in disbelief.

"You let us get taken away by the state because you were too busy partying." Mama paused. "You let my daddy send me to Mississippi with his mama to be beaten by her and raped by his brother." Mama sobbed so hard she could hardly continue her sentence. "I will never forgive you!"

"Clarene, I was young," Grandma pleaded. "I thought you would have a better life if you were away from me. I didn't know they were hurting you. I didn't want you to leave." She stuttered, "I…I just didn't know how to take care of you."

"So what, Momma! That's no excuse. You left us there. That horrible woman treated me like a maid and beat me for existing."

"Clarene, I didn't know." Grandma reached for Mama, but she backed away.

"Of course, you didn't know. You forgot about us while you were here with your real family."

Mama set her gaze upon me, Meechie and Erin. "I bet y'all didn't know I didn't see your grandmother again until I was 17-years-old. That crazy old bitch was too old to take care of us by then, so she sent me back to St. Louis."

Grandma fell back into the chair, overwhelmed by the bomb Mama was sharing with us.

Mama emphasized her words. "She STILL didn't know how to be a mother. She made me cook and clean while Lauren could do what she pleased. That's why she's strung out on that shit now!"

Meechie's eyes grew larger. I could see she wanted to defend Aunt TeeTee, but couldn't find the words. I also think Meechie was afraid that Mama would turn her wrath on her.

Grandma sat up in her chair and spoke up. "Clarene, you know that's a damn lie! I never treated you any different from Lauren and you know it."

Mama raised her voice. "Whatever! All you do is lie, lie, lie."

Grandma got to her feet. "You better watch your mouth when you're talking to me!"

"Or what, Momma?" Mama put her hands on her

hips and rolled her neck. "You're just as messed up as me and you know it. That's why Lorenz got addicted to that shit and killed himself."

I didn't know much about Lorenz. But I remember when Mama got the call that he died. I was around eight-years-old. We were living in Washington in a burgundy house on a hill on the east side of Tacoma.

I can remember hearing the phone ring and Mama weeping a few minutes after. Then she came to me and Sissy and delivered the news—her brother, Uncle Lorenz, was dead. He couldn't have been any more than 30 at the time. She didn't take us to the funeral though. I asked Donny why and he told me and Sissy we were too young. When I was 13, I asked Grandma what happened. She said Lorenz was on drugs and paranoid. He thought someone was chasing him. He ran into a tree three blocks from Grandma's house and died instantly.

Grandma dished Mama a slap so hard it echoed throughout the house. "You watch your goddamn mouth! I'm sick of this. It stops NOW!" Grandma yelled.

Mama held the red side of her face and stared down at Grandma, before balling up her fist and raising it at her.

Steph rushed to defend Grandma. "Clarene, I'm not going to stand here and watch you put your hands on Aunt Rose."

Mama maintained her stance before cracking a devilish smile and breaking her silence. "Old lady, you better be glad…"

"Nah, let her drunk ass through!" Grandma demanded. "The day you put your hands on me will be the day you die. I brought you into this world; I will take your ass out."

Mama backed down. She stood face to face with Grandma in silence. Grandma spoke up. "I don't care what you think about me." Grandma pointed her finger. "If you want to blame me for what you've become, so be it. But this is the last time you will come into MY HOUSE yelling and acting a damn fool. What you need to be worrying about is your own kids."

Mama tried to talk over her, but Grandma stopped her in her tracks. "Like I said, if you don't like it, you can get the hell out of my house!"

"Come on, Nikki. We're leaving!" Mama shouted.

I stood there like a statue cemented into the floor.

"I said, come on!" She grabbed my arm so hard I thought it came out of the socket.

"No! I'm not going anywhere with you!" I pulled my arm back and played tug of war with her.

Steph ran over and pulled my arm away from Mama. Carlos grabbed Mama's waist from behind and picked her up. She screamed, "Let me go, mutherfucka!" She kicked her legs.

"Put her out!" Grandma yelled.

He didn't get a chance to open the door. TeeTee was coming in at the same time.

"Uhhh, what the hell is going on in here?" TeeTee shuffled out of Carlos' way.

Carlos carried Mama to her car, put her down and walked away. Mama charged towards him. "You son of a bitch! Don't you ever put your hands on me again!" She swung at Carlos, but lost her balance and fell to the ground.

She was able to get the assistance of a nearby tree and pulled herself to her feet. But she wasn't finished. "See, Mama! You let that crackhead bitch stay here, but you kick me out!" Grandma did her best to ignore her. "I know you can hear me," she roared from the lawn. "You always loved her more than me. What I gotta do, huh? Smoke crack to get your attention?"

Grandma grew tired of her disruptions. "Clarene, take your ass home before I call the police on you!"

"I ain't going no damn where until you kick that crackhead out!"

I stood by and watched as TeeTee paced the floor and Grandma tried to calm her down.

"That's it. I'm sick of this shit." Aunt TeeTee went outside.

"Oh, shit," Steph said, with her eyes as big as windows.

"Grandma, please get my mama," I begged.

Grandma headed for the door, but paused. "No. Let her get what she's asking for." She walked back to the kitchen and looked out the window. "They've been at it for years. Maybe this is what they need."

I began to weep and slide down the wall until my butt hit the floor. *Oh, my God. What have I done?*

CHAPTER

Seventeen

"HERE COMES MISS Crackhead America!" Mama clapped her hands and laughed.

"You got something to say to me?" Aunt TeeTee stalked towards Mama.

"Yep, you're a no-good crackhead heffa!"

Aunt TeeTee didn't waste any time punching Mama in her mouth.

Mama put her hand over her mouth, noticing blood when she released it. "You bitch!" She swung and hit TeeTee on the side of her face.

It was like a heavyweight boxing match. Mama punched TeeTee then TeeTee punched Mama. They pulled each other's hair then fell in the grass and rolled around, trying to hit one another with their free hand. After a few minutes, they were too tired to continue.

"Okay, y'all. That's enough!" Carlos separated them.

"It ain't over 'til I say it's over." Mama staggered

towards the front porch. The side of her mouth was bloody and grass was all over the back of her purple dress. Clearly, TeeTee had gotten the best of her. Mama gave her dress a tug then crouched like a wrestler with her hands up in waist-high karate chops. "Come on, bitch!" She wobbled. "I ain't done with you!"

"Keep on talking, mess. I'm going to kick yo' ass some more!" TeeTee threatened.

They tried to go for each other again, but Carlos stood in-between them. "That's enough," he ordered.

Steph stood on the front porch, watching and talking under her breath. "This shit is so crazy!" She shook her head. "This is exactly why I live far from this family."

"I ain't got time for this shit!" Aunt TeeTee gave up and went into the house, passing Grandma on her way.

"Yeah," Mama taunted. "I bet you got time for some crack, though." Mama bellowed out a hearty laugh.

"Clarene, it's over. Go home," Grandma demanded.

"Don't worry, I'm leaving! I've been kicked out of better places anyway!" Mama picked up her black clutch bag from the sidewalk and weaved to her car. "I hope you're getting a good look, because this is the last time you'll ever see me!" She smacked her round derriere. "Kiss my ass!" Then got in her car, catching her ankle-length dress in the door. The car peeled out.

Carlos walked up the steps silently before speaking. "Your family is crazy as hell!" He took a deep breath and shook his head before retreating to a nearby chair.

Meechie followed TeeTee to her room and tried to comfort her. "Mama, are you okay?"

"Yeah, I'm fine. I'm sick of Clarene blaming me for

everything." She peeled off her torn shirt and threw it on the bed. "Yeah, I smoke crack. So what! But I'm not a crackhead!" She raised her voice then sat on the bed. Meechie didn't say a word—she just stood in the doorway and listened with tears streaming down her face.

"Ain't nobody ever asked me what happen to me. After losing your daddy and Lorenz, I needed something to numb the pain." TeeTee tilted her head and looked up at Meechie. "I'm tired of being in the streets. I want to stop, but I don't know how."

Meechie moved in closer. "Mama, why don't you go to one of them places that can help you?"

"Like, what? A rehab?" TeeTee scrunched her face.

"Yeah, one of those." Meechie sat down next to her.

"Girl, them places cost. I ain't got no money for that."

"Maybe you can call around and see how much they cost?"

TeeTee chuckled. "Girl, please. I'll be alright." She got up, searched through her dresser drawer and pulled out a black-and-white striped shirt. "Besides, ain't nobody going to help me. It's probably a waste of time, anyway," she replied.

"Mama, you can at least try." Meechie pleaded with her.

TeeTee looked at her then turned and walked out the door. Meechie collapsed on the bed in a fetal position and began to cry and scream. "I hate it here. I don't want to be here anymore!" Her muffled yells reminded me of someone screaming into a pillow. I wanted to go to her, but I didn't feel like I could help her. I wasn't strong enough.

TeeTee walked past the kitchen and out the front door. Grandma ran after her. "Lauren, where are you going?"

"Mama, leave me alone. Okay? I'll be back later." She kept walking.

"Lauren!" Grandma yelled. "If you going to smoke that mess…" Grandma paused. "You are not welcome back at my house. I mean it!"

TeeTee stopped but didn't turn around. A few moments later, she continued on her journey. Grandma stood there with pain in her eyes, watching TeeTee walk off, before walking back to the house. When Grandma came back, Steph, Carlos and I were sitting at the kitchen table.

"Where's Lauren?" Steph asked Grandma, playing with her mid-length tresses.

"She kept on walking. If she comes back here high, I ain't letting her in." Grandma sat down in the dining room chair and kicked off her pink house shoes. "I don't know what to do with them two. Clarene is drunk all the time and Lauren can't stay clean." Grandma turned her chair Steph's way, leaned in and rested her hand on hers.

"Please take them with you," Grandma requested. "Those girls don't deserve this."

"I can see taking Nikki. We just can't take Meechie without Lauren's permission."

"Wait a minute. I'll be right back." Grandma left the room and came back with a yellow envelope in her hand. She handed Steph a paper with a seal on it. "You don't worry about Lauren. I have custody of Meechie and Erin. I'll keep Erin with me, but take Meechie with you. She needs to get away from here, too."

Steph looked down and transitioned into deep thought. Carlos rubbed her back. "Baby, her mama can't take care of her." He paused. "It may be best if she comes with us."

The mood was broken by the sound of a voice behind us. "You should've been and kicked her ass out!" We turned to find Uncle Lee looking in the refrigerator.

"Lee, you been here the whole time?" Steph asked with her hand on her round hip.

"Yep, and I heard everything."

"Why didn't you come help?" Grandma asked, with her eyebrows touching each other.

"Shit, I ain't 'bout to get in the middle of that. I got warrants." Uncle Lee poured himself a cup of juice and headed back down the steps to his room.

Uncle Lee is one to talk. He smokes crack, too. Grandma needs to put his food-stealing self out.

"That boy gets on my nerves," Grandma ranted. "He needs to get his self together, too." She waved her light brown hand. "I'll deal with him later."

The table was silent. Everyone looked rundown. Carlos kept shaking his head. Steph spent the next twenty minutes with her hands on top of her head in deep thought. Grandma sat staring into space with her legs crossed, shaking her feet. I could tell everyone was affected by Mama's rampage, but no was brave enough to talk about it.

I was confused why no one asked Grandma about

Mama's allegations. Did Grandma really leave Mama? Was her guilt the reason why she made so many excuses for Mama?

I couldn't believe that my favorite person in the world was the reason Mama was so bitter. I could no longer hold my tongue. I had to ask.

"Grandma." I paused and looked at her. "What was Mama talking about?"

Grandma didn't break her gaze. "What do you mean, baby?"

"You know… What she said about you leaving her?"

Steph looked up and gave Grandma her full attention. Grandma leaned forward and put her head in her hands and sighed. "It was a long time ago. I was young. I didn't know how to take care of children. I was barely old enough to take care of myself."

I took a deep breath before continuing. "Did you leave her?"

"No, baby. Her and your uncle Michael were taken from me." Grandma wouldn't look up at me. She played with her nails instead.

"But, why?" Tears filled my eyes.

"I couldn't stop drinking and partying." She took a deep breath. "I had a lot of pain in my heart. I thought I could drink them away. Horrible things happened to me when I was in foster care."

I turned my body towards her. "You were in foster care?"

"Yes," she paused. "My mother couldn't take care of us because she was very ill. She had seizures. So the state took me, my brothers and sisters away, and put us in different foster homes."

Grandma looked down as tears fell from her eyes. I was young, but something in my heart understood the pain Grandma explained. It was as though I was sitting across from a much-older Mama. *Is this how Mama feels?* I wondered. Hearing Grandma profess her tenderness gave me hope that one day Mama would get well enough to take responsibility for her actions too.

"I was shuffled around—each time a new family. They treated me bad. I was beaten and molested so many times I lost count. By the time I had your Mama and Michael, I was broken. I could hardly think straight. So my social worker took them and put them in foster care."

"Were they there for a long time?" I asked.

"No. My ex-husband—your grandfather—came and got them and took them down South to be raised by his mother." She sat up straight in her chair and looked me in the eye. "I had no idea they were being mistreated."

"Well, why didn't you go get them?"

"I felt they would be better off there." Her tone grew soft. "And… I was embarrassed and scared they would reject me."

"Why didn't you tell me, Grandma?" I wiped the tears from my eyes.

"I didn't know how to tell you. I'm sorry, Nikki Pooh." She grabbed my hand and gently squeezed it.

I snatched it back. "This is all your fault, Grandma." I stood up. "If you didn't leave my Mama, maybe she would be a better mother."

"Nikki, calm down," Steph said, moving her hand

up and down.

"No! You lied to me!" I yelled at Grandma. "You told me to be patient with Mama and one day she would change, but you knew you were the reason she acted that way." I wept.

Grandma came over and wrapped her arms around me tightly. Although, I wanted to resist, the wounded child within me desired her embrace. I put my head on her shoulder. "Baby, I'm sorry. I didn't think you would understand. I'm human. I make mistakes too. I wish I could take it all back, but all I can do is do my best." She rubbed my back. Tears fell from my eyes, soaking her blue shirt.

"What's wrong?" Meechie asked, standing at the kitchen entrance. She surprised us. We were silent.

"Y'all ain't going to tell me?" Meechie folded her arms. "Grandma, what happened? Why are you hugging Nikki like that? Did something happen to Aunt Clarene?"

"Come in here and sit down, Meechie." Meechie sat next to me, locking her fingers on the table. Grandma sat next to her.

"I've always been there the best way I could for you and your cousins. But… I blame myself for your mother being on drugs." Tears rolled down her cheeks. "I didn't know how to be a mom to my kids, so I tried to be their friends. I let your mom, aunts and uncles drink and smoke weed with me and my friends."

"What?" Meechie looked at Grandma in disbelief.

Carlos interrupted. "Steph, I think we should take Erin and Sissy to the store or something so they can talk." They got up and walked out, calling Sissy and Erin from the back where they were watching TV in Grandma's room.

"Erin and Sissy!"

They both ran to the living room. Sissy spoke up. "Are we leaving now?"

Steph rubbed her head. "No, not yet. But do you want to go to the store?"

They both went crazy with excitement. "Yeah!"

"Get your shoes and come on."

When Erin and Sissy ran to the back room to get their shoes, Steph gave Grandma a nod and walked out the front door to wait for them to come out.

Meechie waited until Erin closed the door behind her before she continued. "Why would you do that?" Meechie's voice squeaked.

Grandma held up her hand. "Please let me finish. Then they started using heavier drugs and I couldn't stop them. So I pretended like I didn't see it. When Lorenz died, I felt so guilty. Losing a child is never easy, but I feel if I would've been a better parent, he would still be here today."

Meechie looked at Grandma strongly, before getting up and walking out the front door. Grandma sat there and watched, with her elbows on the table and her fingers interlocked. I got up and followed Meechie, yelling her name from the front porch before going after her. By the time I caught up to her, her skinny legs had carried her up the street and onto Gladys Avenue.

"Where are you going?" I called to her.

Meechie didn't answer. Out of breath, I yelled at her.

"Mee-chie, where are you going?!"

She stopped walking and turned to me. "I don't know! Dang!" She kept on walking.

I ran after her until I could match her pace. "I know you're mad, but at least hear Grandma out."

Meechie kept her eyes focused on her mission. "I don't want to hear nothing she got to say."

Tears were streaming down her face and into the corners of her mouth. "She's the reason my mama's on drugs. She makes me sick!"

Although I agreed that Grandma hadn't been the best parent and had played a huge role in TeeTee's drug addiction, I was old enough to know both of our mamas had a choice. Meechie, however, wasn't understanding.

"What kind of mama does drugs with their kids? I mean, what did she think was going to happen?" Meechie kept her stride, only stopping to cross the railroad tracks.

"You can't really blame Grandma. It's TeeTee's fault she won't stop using drugs."

I must've hit a nerve. Meechie stopped in the middle of the street and set her sights on me. "What?" She walked closer and stopped right as the tip of her shoes met mine. *Oh, man, am I going to fight Meechie? Damn, when is this day ever going to end?*

I thought she was going to punch me, but she expressed her anger instead. "Yes it is! Grandma knew she wasn't doing right by her kids. She knew she was the reason my mama is on drugs, but she pretended like nothing ever happened. I bet if your Mama didn't come over here and tell everybody what happened, we still wouldn't know." Meechie walked off.

"Maybe Grandma was trying to protect us!" I called from behind her.

Meechie stopped, turned around and walked back towards me. "Grandma don't give a damn about nobody but herself. If she did, she would've done a better job raising our mamas. What about me and Erin, huh? Why do we have to suffer because Grandma had a secret?" Meechie's voice grew louder.

"I'm tired of people calling my Mama a crackhead!" She bellowed, "You know what I'm more tired of? Her acting like one, stealing my money, leaving us, coming home high! I'm sick of it! That money is all I have." Meechie began to sob. "How else would I take care of myself?" she cried. "So... what? We're all supposed to suffer because she feels guilty? That's bullshit and you know it!" She pointed at me repeatedly.

I was at a loss for words. I'd never seen Meechie that mad. Nor had I ever heard her curse that much. I tried to reason with her but I couldn't get a word in.

"My question is...," she quieted her tone as she got closer to me. "How can you forgive her, knowing she's the reason your Mama is a bitter old bit—"

Before Meechie could get the rest of the word out, I cautioned her. "Meechie, don't be talking about my mama like that!"

Meechie moved in closer. "Or what, Nikki? You gonna tell your Mama on me? News flash! She don't give a damn about you. Just like my Mama rather be out smoking crack than taking care of me and Erin!" Meechie yelled so loud an older black man came out on his porch and fussed at us.

"Hey, y'all better get from in front of my house with all that damn yelling! Where y'all live at?"

Me and Meechie walked off.

"I know you heard me talking to you," he called from his porch.

I ignored his rants and focused on getting Meechie to come back to the house. "Come on. Let's go back home. It's getting dark."

"No. Leave me alone!" She walked away. I stood there and watched until she disappeared into the distance, then walked back to Grandma's with Meechie's words dancing in my ears.

I also thought about how badly Mama had acted that day. I wished she would stop drinking long enough to see how messed up she'd become. More importantly, I couldn't get the sting out of my heart that Grandma had put there. I thought my grandma was perfect. An angel. But she wasn't. She was as messed up as Mama. That was a fact I couldn't swallow.

I got back to the house in one piece, but the pain of what I was carrying weighed me down. I felt tired. As I reached for the door handle, I heard TeeTee's voice from the other side of the door. *TeeTee's back?*

Instead of opening the door, I stood there and listened for any sounds of chaos. I didn't hear any.

When I came in, I saw her, Steph and Grandma sitting at the kitchen table. TeeTee didn't look high. I guess Grandma's threat must've knocked some sense into her.

"Where's Meechie?" TeeTee asked.

"I don't know." I pulled out a chair to rest for a moment. "I tried to get her to come back, but she kept on walking up Park Lane."

Aunt TeeTee stood. "Wait a minute. It's dark outside. I'm about to go find my baby."

Your baby? Just a few hours ago she was going to get high. Now she cares?

"Sit down, Lauren," Grandma ordered. "Give her some time. She'll be back."

TeeTee sat down. "What have I done to my kids?" TeeTee put her forehead on the table.

Steph spoke up. "Let me take Meechie for a while."

TeeTee raised her head from the table. "To Washington? That's too far. I don't know about that."

Grandma interjected, "Lauren, you need some help. Let Meechie go and see something different. At least you know she's going to be safe." Grandma paused. "And...if you don't go to treatment, you can't stay here anymore and Erin ain't going with you."

TeeTee looked like she was out of options. I held my breath in suspense, waiting for TeeTee to answer. Before she could, Meechie came in the door.

"Mama, you back?" Meechie stood in the entrance of the dining room.

TeeTee stood. "Yes. I'm so sorry. I didn't realize how much I was hurting you and Erin." TeeTee began to cry. "I'm going to rehab and when I get out, I promise I'll do better."

Meechie let out a sigh and ran and hugged TeeTee. "Thank you, Mama."

TeeTee raised Meechie's chin. "Listen, I want you to

get your stuff together. You're going with Steph for a while until I can get better."

Meechie hugged TeeTee once more, tightly, and went to her room to retrieve her bag.

I was relieved that I didn't have to leave Meechie behind. Also, I was happy she'd gotten a happy ending. I knew I wouldn't see Mama for a long time. It hurt, but I knew for now I was better off without her.

I prayed I could find it in my heart to forgive Grandma. Although she lied to me, I felt she was trying to protect me in her own way. I hoped one day I would find my daddy. California wasn't that far from Washington. Knowing that he would be a few states over made me feel closer to him.

"Come on, y'all. It's getting late. We have to go," Steph insisted. Steph called to Sissy, "Get your stuff together. We have a long ride ahead of us."

Grandma embraced Steph. "Thank you for taking them."

Grandma hugged me tight and whispered in my ear. "I know you're mad at me, but I told you I would take care of things." I kissed her on the cheek and whispered back. "Thank you, Grandma. I love you SO much!"

Meechie, Sissy and I said our final goodbyes to Grandma, TeeTee and Erin and packed into Carlos' brown Buick Regal.

As he pulled away, Grandma stood on the steps waving and crying. I watched until I could no longer see the outline of her hourglass figure. When I turned around, I closed my eyes and laid my head on Meechie's shoulder. Tears swam down my face as I watched the streetlights flicker through my eyelids. I knew leaving St. Louis was only the beginning of my journey, but I didn't care. Anywhere was better than there.

CHAPTER

Eighteen

WE MADE IT OVER to Uncle Robert's house after 11:00 p.m. Uncle Robert was Donny's middle brother. Although he wasn't my real uncle, I liked calling him "Uncle" because he was always nice to me. Uncle Robert lived in a suburb of St. Louis called University City – or U-City, as St. Louis residents commonly called it – with his wife, Kim and daughter, Marie. Their house was a nice two-story brick home that smelled of cinnamon every time I came over.

Once there, Steph told us to get some sleep because we were leaving for Mississippi early in the morning. She showed us to the guest bedroom, said goodnight and closed the door. A few moments later, I came out to look for the bathroom. While I wandered around, I could hear Steph on the phone.

"Yeah, I got her. Clarene acted like a fool. She came over Aunt Rose's house drunk. Her and Lauren got into a fight, too. Don't worry, I made sure Sissy didn't see it.

Daddy, I'm bringing Nikki and Meechie back with me, too. They're not safe here. I may need you to help us with them, okay? Well, we're leaving in the morning to go to Biloxi. I'll call you when we get there. I love you, too. Bye."

After using the bathroom, I came back in the room and slid under the covers of the queen-sized bed I shared with Sissy and Meechie. They were already asleep. I laid there for a while and prayed before drifting off to sleep.

Dear God, Thank you for rescuing me and Meechie. Please look over Mama. She needs your help. Amen.

After all that had gone on that day, talking to God was the only thing that made me feel better. I don't remember going to sleep, but I recall the flash of light that woke us from our sleep in the wee hours of the morning.

"Get up, y'all. It's time to get ready to go," Steph whispered.

"What time is it?" I asked with a crackle in my voice.

"It's 4:30. Hurry up, so we can hit the highway before rush hour."

I dragged myself out of Uncle Robert's comfortable bed and searched for my shoes. Meechie was so tired she couldn't release herself from the edge of the bed. However, I had no problem getting Sissy up. She was excited to leave St. Louis.

"Did Steph tell you where we're going?" Mee-chie asked as she stretched.

"Yeah, Mississippi," I answered, looking under the bed for my other shoe.

Meechie put her foot in her shoe. "What's in Mississippi?

"I think Carlos is from there. We're going to see his family for a few days, somewhere called Biloxi. Then we're driving back to Washington."

"How you know?" Meechie twisted up her lips and poked out her neck like a chicken.

"I heard her on the phone talking to Donny last night." I finished stuffing my clothes into my book bag, then left the room to meet Steph and Carlos in the living room.

"Y'all got everything?" Carlos asked.

"Yeah."

"Make sure, because once we leave we ain't coming back," Steph added.

Carlos grabbed our bags and headed for the car. Steph stayed behind and thanked Uncle Robert for his hospitality before we took off to the Magnolia State. Meechie and Sissy went back to sleep in the car. I stayed up and watched the flashing lights of the cars on the highway. "How long will it take to get there?" I asked.

Carlos answered in his deep manly voice, "About 10 hours if we drive all the way through. We should get there around four o'clock."

Steph interrupted. "Try to get some rest. We have a long ride ahead of us."

I tried to sleep, but my mind kept wandering. I thought about what it would be like to be in Washington without Mama. Then, I thought about if I would see her again—or if I even wanted too.

I checked my coat pocket to make sure I still had my

daddy's number. *When I get to Washington, I'm going to find him.* I stared at the paper with his name penned on it and spoke to him. *Daddy, I hope I find you. I want to get to know you. Mama can't take care of me. I hope you can.* I kissed the paper and put it in my bra, next to my heart.

Between thoughts, I could hear Steph and Carlos chatting quietly. I guess they thought I was sleep.

"Are you sure we can handle such a big responsibility?" Carlos asked.

"I don't know. But, they don't have anywhere else to go." She paused. "If we didn't take them, God knows what would've happened."

Carlos sat with his thoughts before replying. "I get that, but how are we going to take care of two extra mouths when we're barely making it now?"

"My daddy said he'll help and I'll see if we can get some assistance from the state. We'll make it work."

Steph and Carlos continued to make plans, but masked their anxiety with music from the radio. I diverted my attention from eavesdropping to singing the lyrics to *Hanging on Strings* by Loose Ends in my head while tapping my foot. The song reminded me of the good ole' days back in Washington when Mama and her friends would drink, listen to music and play cards. She would get drunk and call me out of my room to perform the latest dances for her friends.

Deep down, I wished I would see Mama again. I dreaded the fact that I couldn't see her face, even though she spent most of the time yelling at me. However, I knew it was time to take care of myself, no matter the cost.

The rest of our journey to Biloxi was pegged with '80s

jams, singing, periods of horseplay, and the overwhelming sense of restlessness we felt from being cooped up in Carlos' car for 10 long hours.

We arrived in Mississippi that afternoon around 4:00, just as Carlos promised. The town of Biloxi looked old. A far cry from the city life in St. Louis. Just like St. Louis, there were brown people everywhere. As we made twists and turns through the city, I noticed people sitting on the front porches of their wooden bungalows, watching for any sense of excitement a passerby could spare. In a nutshell, it was country.

Before we made it to Carlos' mom's house, we stopped at a local chicken spot a few blocks from our destination. Once inside, Carlos was greeted with a big hug from a portly, dark-skinned gentleman waiting nearby for his food.

"Hey, man!" the man happily announced with open arms. He hugged Carlos tight and patted him on his back.

"Hey Quincy, man! What you been up to?"

"Awww, nothing, man. You know—trying to make a dollar out of fifteen cents." The man rubbed his belly and finished with a deep laugh.

Carlos burst into laughter. "Cuz, you crazy!"

The man turned his attention to me, Sissy and Meechie. "And, who are these beautiful young ladies you have with you?"

Carlos stuck out his arm, placing his hand on my right shoulder. "Oh, these are my wife's cousins, Nikki, Sissy and Michelle—I mean Meechie."

Meechie hated to be called Michelle—her first name. Sometimes, I would call her by it just to mess with her.

"I'm your cousin, Quincy."

"Hey," we all answered.

"Y'all are some pretty young ladies. Carlos, you gon' have to keep your eyes on them."

I couldn't shake how funny he sounded. He talked too country and too fast. I could hardly understand him. I was kind of freaked out by his comments, so I drew my attention to the overhead menu. Meechie followed. "He's a horny old man." Meechie expressed. I put my hand over my mouth to contain my laughter.

"Y'all go ahead and order what you want." Carlos said, momentarily leaving his conversation with Quincy. He went back to talking to the man, while me, Meechie and Sissy studied the menu. Soon after, Steph joined us.

"You guys alright?" her voice probed from behind us.

I turned to answer and found a red-eyed Steph standing behind me. "Yeah…Are you okay?"

Steph's silence spoke for her before she opened her mouth. "Yeah, I'm okay. It's been a long couple of days. I think I need some rest. Plus, I miss my kids."

Steph left her kids, Deon and Alisha, with Donny until she came back. I was surprised. Steph was very protective of her children. I'm sure it took a lot to leave them behind.

"Do they have chicken nuggets here?" Sissy inquired.

"No, Sissy this ain't McDonald's," Steph responded. "Just pick something and come on, girl."

Meechie and I placed our order, then stood back and

listened to Steph and Sissy fuss over her meal.

"How long we supposed to be staying here?" Meechie asked, rubbing her eyes.

"I don't know, but I hope not long. I'm ready to get to Washington."

I wanted to ask Carlos, but he was still knee slapping with Quincy by the door. Finally, a short, dark-skinned lady with braids called to Quincy from behind the counter. "Q, your order is ready."

"Alright, baby. Here I come."

Quincy grabbed his bag then looked inside the red and white plastic bag to ensure everything was there. "Thank you, baby. Tell your mama I said hi," he said to the cashier. He headed towards the door.

"It was nice meeting you pretty ladies. 'Los, remember to stop by and see Gina before you leave." He pointed at Carlos.

"Alright, man. I'll see you later."

As Carlos walked back to us, Steph met him halfway. "Let's get our food to go. I'm ready to sit down and rest."

The cashier bagged our food and off we went. A few blocks later, we stopped in front of a white house with green shutters and a partial chain link fence.

"Alright, y'all. We're here," Carlos announced, then honked the horn.

"This is it?" I whispered to Meechie.

She looked at me sideways. "I guess so."

A round lady and tall, dark-skinned guy who looked like Carlos came out of the house and met us at the car.

"Hey, 'Los." She hugged him. "It's so nice to see you!"

Steph got out and stood there, but the lady didn't acknowledge her. Carlos sensed the awkwardness, so he filled the gap by introducing us to her. "Meechie, Sissy and Nikki, this is my mama, Betty."

"It's nice to meet you young ladies."

We all took turns saying hello.

"Oh, and this one of my brothers, Twin." Carlos put his hand on his back.

"Twin?" I looked at Meechie. "That's a weird name."

"How ya'll doing? Ya'll need help with your bags?" Twin flashed a smile and looked me and Meechie up and down.

"Umm, I guess so. Our bags are in the trunk." I responded.

"What's up with the men around here?" Meechie asked.

I hunched my shoulders then helped Steph grab the food out of the car. Betty led the way to the house.

"Y'all come on in and make yourself comfortable. Twin, put they stuff next to the couch." She pointed to a fashionable-looking green couch with plastic on it. The house smelled musty, like someone needed to open a window. I could tell someone had been cooking because the house smelled of chicken grease and cornbread.

"I sure hope y'all are hungry."

"We already got something to eat."

"What? Why would you do that? I told you I was cooking." Betty put her hands on her round hips.

"That's alright," she chuckled and waved her hand. "There's plenty for later."

Me, Meechie and Sissy sat at the table to eat our food, while Carlos and his family chatted in the background. Carlos' brother came and sat next to us. "How old are y'all?"

I almost choked trying to answer, so Meechie spoke up. "Too young for you." She bit into her chicken leg and rolled her eyes.

"Y'all look grown enough to me." He cracked a devilish smile, exposing his crooked front tooth. I was sure Twin wasn't our age. He looked to be in his early 20s. *Dang, he can't find a girl his age?* I spoke up. "Well, we ain't. Were only 14."

Twin looked at me. "Girl, if you was a little older, I would make you mine."

His comment made me feel uncomfortable. I grabbed Meechie's leg and scooted closer for protection.

"If you don't mind, we trying to eat our food," Meechie snapped.

"You got a smart little mouth, don't you? You betta be careful. One day it might get you hurt." Twin smiled and got up from the table.

"What the hell?" Meechie looked at me. "The people here are weird. I'll be happy when we leave."

"Yeah, me too."

"I think he likes you, Nikki," Sissy teased.

"Ewww, that's nasty. He's too old."

"If he starts getting too fresh, tell Steph." Meechie insisted.

"I will. Hopefully, he's not that stupid."

While we finished eating our food, I looked over and

noticed Steph sitting by herself. Carlos was laughing and catching up with his family, but she seemed uncomfortable. Kind of the way a person looks when they don't fit in.

"I don't think Carlos' family likes Steph." I whispered to Meechie.

"Why you say that?"

"Mrs. Betty didn't even talk to Steph and the rest of them ain't really saying nothing to her either."

The door opened and a man who looked identical to Twin came in. "Oh, he's a twin." I said.

Meechie looked at me and snickered. "Duh."

We laughed. "I hope he's not as creepy as the other one."

"Hey!" Carlos yelled and hugged him tight. "What's up, Two?" Twin's twin, 'Two,' looked identical to Twin. If it wasn't for the red baseball cap he was wearing, I wouldn't have been able to tell them apart. He hardly spoke to us when Carlos introduced him.

Eventually, Steph grew tired of the noise and went in a back room. We didn't see her for the rest of the night. Me, Meechie and Sissy transitioned from the table to the living room and watched TV until all of the guests left one by one. Carlos left with them to hang out at a local bar. Betty brought us some blankets and encouraged us to make a pallet on the floor.

Before checking out for the night, I went in the kitchen to get something to drink. I turned on the light and hundreds of roaches filled the floor and the stove where somebody neglected to pick up the food.

"Ewww!" I couldn't help but vocalize my disgust.

"What's wrong with you?" Meechie called from the

living room.

"They got roaches and a lot of them."

"What you think they going to do? Bite you?" Meechie laughed.

"Let me see." Sissy ran into the kitchen. "That's nasty." She backed away.

I started to retreat, but I was thirsty. I waited until the bugs hid under the stove and refrigerator, then found a cup and washed it three times before I got some juice out of the refrigerator.

When I returned to our pallet, I laid at the end, behind Sissy. I checked under the covers for bugs, said my prayers and then drifted off to sleep.

Early in the morning, I could hear Steph and Carlos arguing. I sat up and listened, catching a few sentences of their dispute.

"You know your family don't like me. Why you leave me here?"

"Why is you tripping? I wasn't even gone that long."

"Carlos, its three o'clock in the morning. Look at you, all drunk and shit. I'm ready to go!"

"Steph, we just got here."

"So what! If you ain't ready to leave by tomorrow, I'm leaving without you!"

I looked around to see if Meechie was up to gossip with, but she was in a deep coma-like sleep. After sitting up for a little while longer, I lay back down and eventually fell asleep.

A couple of hours later, I heard the front door open and close. I didn't think anything of it. I ignored the noise and tried my best to go back to sleep.

Next, I was shaken out of my sleep by two large

hands pulling me away from Sissy and Meechie and covering my mouth. I tried to fight, but he was too strong. He smelled of alcohol and cologne as he whispered in my ear, "You better not say a word or I'm going to get the other two, too." *I know this voice.* I screamed, but the screams were muffled by his large, dark-skinned hand.

I struggled, but he held me tighter, wrapping his leg around mine and spreading it apart. He pulled down my panties with his free hand, unzipped his pants and pulled me closer to him. I kicked and elbowed him. But it didn't matter. He had his grip on me. I was helpless and too weak to fight him. He licked his hand and put his spit on my vagina, then thrust his penis inside of me.

The pain of his penis ripping through me was unbearable. I tried to push it out of me, but each time he held me tighter and pumped harder. Tears streamed down my face as he continued to violate me. Eventually, everything got dark.

When I woke up, it was light outside. Hoping it was a dream, I checked for my panties. They weren't pulled all the way up. I wrapped the blanket around me and went into the bathroom. I pulled down my panties and sat on the toilet and noticed there was blood in them. I tried to pee but it hurt too bad. As I wiped, blood and clear stuff was on the tissue.

I cried and wiped vigorously, until I couldn't see anything else on the tissue. *Who did this to me?*

I went over the events in my head. I hoped I'd find a clue to who had taken liberty with me. The first person who popped in my head was Twin. I cried and cried until I was strong enough to come out of the bathroom.

I went searching for Steph, but she was nowhere in sight. I went to the living room to tell Meechie, but she was gone too.

Sissy was watching cartoons and eating a bowl of cereal. "Where is Meechie and Steph?"

"They left." Sissy didn't take her eyes off of the TV.

"Where did they go?"

"Back to Washington."

"What?" I sat on the couch in disbelief. "Without us?"

"Yeah. She told me we're going to ride back with Carlos tomorrow."

How could she leave us? I melted into the plastic couch. *I knew I couldn't trust her. I guess some things never change.*

CHAPTER

Nineteen

I FELT COLD INSIDE, like all of the parts that made a young woman had been hollowed out. I yearned to get his stink off of me. The smell of his cheap cologne under my nose made my stomach ache.

I recounted the voice that whispered those repulsive words in my ear the night before. He sounded like Twin, but he and Two were identical. It could have been either one of them. I transitioned between feeling perplexed, guilty, angry and vengeful. I wanted to expose the creep who had forcibly taken my dignity away. *But, which one was it?*

"I need to take a bath." I dug in my bag for a fresh pair of panties and went to the bathroom. Unlike the rest of the house, the bathroom looked rather clean. I ran the water, peeled off my bloodstained underwear and got in the tub before it was full.

I scrubbed my skin so hard it became red. I washed between my legs repeatedly then coiled the wash rag tight enough to that I could get the remainder of him from within me.

Why me? I asked, scrubbing my neck and chest. *Who do I tell? Steph's left me. And, I don't know which one of them did it.* I felt guilty and scared at the same time. *Was this my fault?* I replayed the events from the day before in my head. *Did I look at him wrong? Were my pants too tight? God, what did I do to deserve this?* The thought of him inside of me made me want to vomit. I scrubbed harder, until my skin was so raw I could hardly touch it. I stayed in the water until it was cold.

When I got out, I took my time wiping the water from my body and examining my crevices for any sign of the trauma. Between my thighs there were two grapefruit-sized bruises. Uncertain as to how to treat them, I rubbed the bruises with alcohol that I found on the counter. Then I began the painstaking process of dressing my lower body.

I opened the door and walked into Twin as he passed by.

"Oh, what's up little mama?" He barely made eye contact with me.

"What's up?" I couldn't believe the balls on him. "Don't 'what's up' me. I know what you did to me last night." I looked deep into his eyes.

He kept on walking. "I don't know what you talking about." He turned and smirked.

"Yes, you do!" I dropped my clothes and faced off with him.

"Little Mama, I don't know what you talkin' about, but you best get out of my face."

Our exchange began to get the attention of everyone

in the house. I could see Sissy standing in front of the TV.

"You're a pedophile and you know it." Tears ran down my cheeks. "You know what you did to me last night. I heard your voice." I pointed my finger in his face.

Betty came from the back room. "What is going on in here?"

His face got serious. "Mama, she thinks I touched her or something."

"Nah, you did more than touch me. You raped me!"

"Little girl, I didn't do nothing to you. I wasn't even here last night."

Carlos came out of the room, half asleep. "What's going on?"

"'Los, man, this little bitch is accusing me of raping her."

"Bitch?" I yelled. "I'm not your bitch!" I pushed Twin as hard as I could in his chest. He cocked back his hand in retaliation, but before he could connect, Carlos stopped him.

"Whoa, whoa, whoa!" He jumped between us. "Man, what the hell you thinking? She's a little girl."

"You nasty!" I yelled, reaching over Carlos to get a glimpse of Twin. "Raping little girls. What's wrong—you can't find somebody your age?"

I hit a nerve. "'Los, you better get her!"

Betty interjected, "Now young lady, don't go making allegations you can't prove. Did you see him touch you?"

"No…because he held me from behind. I couldn't see his face."

"Well, how you know it was my boy?"

"I heard his voice. And earlier he was looking at me all freaky, telling me I was going to be his girlfriend."

"Bitch, that don't prove nothing!" He turned to Betty. "Mama, she's trying to get me locked up." He tried to get past Carlos, but was unsuccessful.

"Wait a minute now..." Betty held up her hand like a stop sign. "Ain't nobody getting locked up. She don't even know who touched her. For all I know, she could be making it all up."

"Making it up? Why would I do that?"

"Carlos told me you had some troubles back in St. Louis."

"What? What does that have to do with anything?"

"I'm just saying, you don't have any proof it was him, do you?"

"No...I mean, yes..." I stuttered. "I'm sure it was him."

"Are you sure?"

"It was him. I know it!"

"But, do you have any proof?" Betty leaned in.

"No. But...." I felt ganged up on. My heart was beating fast. I could hardly catch my breath.

"I didn't think so." She looked at Carlos. "'Los, let him go." Carlos released his grip. Twin straightened his shirt and gave me a menacing look. "Twin, I think you need to leave for a little while until we get things figured out." Betty pointed at the door.

"But Mama, I didn't do anything," he argued back.

"Boy, you better get yo' ass out of here," she said from a place deep within her being.

My voice crackled. "You just going to let him leave?"

No one responded. Twin went in his room and came back dressed in a pair of white Nikes and a denim jacket with the sleeves cut off. As he passed, I smelled a familiar scent. "Wait! That's the cologne I smelled last night! It was him, I told you!" I tried to fight my way past Carlos, but he was too strong.

"You can't let him leave. You have to call the police!" I begged Carlos.

"Calm down, Nikki. We're going to get to the bottom of this. I promise." I could see Carlos was torn. He felt sorry for me, but he didn't want his brother to go to jail either. The closer Twin got to the door, the more insistent I became.

"Please believe me, Carlos," I requested, tears wetting the rim of my purple t-shirt. But he looked away and didn't say a word. As Twin reached for the door handle, I broke through Carlos and jumped on Twin's back.

"Nikki!" Sissy shouted.

"Oh shit!" Carlos echoed.

"Carlos, get that child!" Betty shrieked in a panic.

I hit him as hard and as many times as I could in his head and face. "You raped me! You're a goddamn pervert! I hope you die!"

Twin tried to block my punches, but was unsuccessful. Eventually, he grew tired of my hits. He reached over his head, grabbed the collar of my shirt and flung me off of him. I hit my head on the wall and fell to the floor. "I told you to get off of me, little girl!" Twin mocked me.

Sissy and Carlos ran to me. "Nikki, you alright?"

I was a little dazed but conscious. The room was

spinning, causing me to weave from side to side. I could hear the muffled pleas of Betty. "Twin, get the hell out of here!" He left as fast as he could. I looked up and Carlos and Sissy were staring down at me.

"Oh, my God! Girl, what was you thinking?" Carlos exclaimed. I didn't answer. "Can you hear me?" He snapped his fingers by each of my ears.

"Her nose is bleeding," Sissy cried.

Betty put a pillow under my head. "Get a towel from the bathroom."

Sissy hurried back and wiped my nose. Betty fanned me with a piece of cardboard she found on the floor.

"Nikki, are you alright?" Carlos asked once more.

My voice crackled. "Yeah, I'm alright."

"Sit her up and give her something to drink." Betty handed Carlos a cup of water. I was a little dazed, but okay.

"How many fingers am I holding up?" Carlos asked.

"Two," I responded.

He looked at my eyes. "I don't think she has a concussion."

"Carlos, why did y'all let him leave? He hurt me."

"Sweetheart, don't worry about that. You worry about getting better."

Betty looked over his shoulder. "Don't you let that girl go to sleep. The last thing I need is her going into a coma."

"Mama, she's alright. Did you forget I'm a medic in the army?"

"I want you to call that wife of yours and have her come and get these children. I don't need no trouble 'round here."

I sat on the floor for a while to gain my composure. Then I shifted myself from the floor to the green plastic-covered couch. Sissy came over and sat next to me.

"Nikki. Did he really do those things to you?"

I stared at the wall while tears streamed down my face. "Yes."

She paused. "Why didn't they call the police?"

I bent over, putting my head in my lap. "I don't know. I guess they don't believe me."

"Tell Steph. I know she'll do something." She stroked my back. I sat up to acknowledge her touch. She laid her head on my shoulder. I loved Sissy's innocence. I wished I could live there with her. The thought of her growing up and life having its way with her hurt me. I wanted her to stay young forever, but I knew that would never happen.

Sissy watched Power Rangers. I was lost in thought, until I heard Carlos' voice near me.

"Steph's plane doesn't land for another 30 minutes. I left a message with Donny to have her call me as soon as she gets in."

I didn't take my eyes off the wall. "Alright."

My head was pounding, but my heart was heavier. I couldn't believe I'd come all that way to have something so heinous and unfortunate happen to me. As bad as things were in St. Louis, being violated in my sleep by a grown man had never crossed my mind. It was the worst thing I'd ever felt in my life. I would've rather felt Mama's punches and have her leave me without food for weeks, then ever experience what he did to me that night. My family was messed up, but they would never let anyone get away with doing that and live to talk about it.

Time went by and, before I knew it, Steph was on the line with Carlos. I could hear Carlos explaining what happened to her. I was kind of relieved to hear that she was upset.

"Here's the phone," Carlos called to me.

I slowly made my way to the phone, holding the tender side of my head.

"Hello."

"What's going on there, Nikki?"

Why does it sound like she's mad at me?

"That man touched me last night."

"What do you mean he touched you?"

"Last night, when I was sleeping, he came in, covered my mouth and raped me."

Steph took a deep breath. "Did you see him?"

"No. I think I passed out."

"Now, Nikki. You're making some strong allegations. Think hard."

"Steph, it was him."

"Why didn't you scream?"

"He told me not to or he was going to get Meechie and Sissy, too. I was scared."

Steph was silent. "That doesn't make any sense, Nikki. You could've kicked until you woke up Meechie and Sissy. They were right by you."

"I couldn't. He was holding me too tight."

"Are you sure you didn't do anything to lead him on?"

"What?" I was confused. "Like what?"

"I don't know. Give him any idea that you liked him."

I began to cry. "No! Why does it sound like you

trying to blame me for what happened?"

"I'm just saying. Sometimes girls make things up."

"I ain't making it up. He raped me."

"So, you don't even know if it was Twin. And you hauled off and hit him? What's wrong with you? I knew you were going to be trouble."

"How is this my fault?" My eyebrows touched each other and I stood up tall. "If you didn't leave me here, none of this would've happened."

Steph's tone changed. "Look, what's going on between me and Carlos ain't your business. I'm going to have my daddy get you and Sissy a ticket. Tell Carlos I'll call him back with the information." She hung up.

I stood there stunned, with the phone in my hand. I couldn't believe what I'd just heard. "Oh my God, she doesn't believe me." I let the phone drop to the floor and rested in a nearby chair. *God, what have I done to deserve this?*

I knew then I could never trust Steph. She was just as messed up as Mama and the rest of them. Contrary to my belief, the grass definitely was not greener on the other side. It was obvious her and Carlos had problems. From that moment, I knew I had to get away from her.

My plan was to get to California to find my daddy. *If I can't find him, I'll live on the streets.* I felt nobody wanted me. It seemed everywhere I went, I was being thrown away.

It hurt to hear that Steph didn't believe me. Had her hate for me allowed her to distrust her intuition? Either way, I no longer trusted her. *When I get back to Washington, I'm leaving, and nobody on this planet is going to stop me—not even God.*

CHAPTER

Twenty

DEAR GOD,

I've been in Washington for two months now and I hate it. I mean, I like being here—it's pretty. The air is fresh and the people smile at you for no reason, but things haven't been right since me and Sissy came back from Mississippi. Steph and Carlos are always arguing and fighting. Mainly about her drinking too much and him cheating on her with some chick at work.

Meechie loves it here. She thinks Washington is better than St. Louis. She told me she never wants to go back again. I don't. I would rather be with my daddy. I keep the paper with his name and number close to my heart. Sometimes, I try to call the number, hoping one day he'll pick up, but it's still disconnected. I pray one day soon I'll get to go to California. Will you tell him that

I'm here? Amen.

* * *

SOON AFTER WE GOT to Washington, Steph left Carlos and we moved into a blue rambler on the Southside of Tacoma. It was nice. Me and Meechie had to share a room, but I didn't care. I enjoyed talking to her. I hadn't seen Sissy much since Steph dropped her off at Donny's that night. Steph stayed in the car, while I went in to thank him for sending for me. When I walked up, he was standing by the doorway helping Sissy with her bags.

"Hi, Donny! I missed you." I gave him a hug, but he barely embraced me back. Maybe he really thinks I'm a gang member.

"Hey kid. How are you doing?" He drew his attention to Sissy. "Little girl, don't leave your stuff by the door. Put it in your room."

"I'm okay."

"You've gotten so big. You're a young lady now."

I smiled.

The house looked the same. The only change was the olive green paint on the walls. As I looked around, I remembered me and Sissy playing the games we got from our Saturday morning scavenger hunts.

"Donny, I really don't want to live with Steph. Can I stay here with you and Sissy?"

He took a seat at the oak kitchen table and invited

me to do the same. "I don't know if that's a good idea."

My heart fluttered. "Why?"

"Well, I'm never home. Also, I don't have enough room."

I felt like he was lying to cover up the fact that he didn't want me there. "What happened to the spare room?"

He paused. "Oh, it's a storage room now." He got up from the table and poured himself a cup of coffee. "I think its best that you stay with Steph for now," he said. "But hey, you can come over whenever you want." He grinned.

I wanted to challenge him, but I didn't. "Okay." I got up and walked to the door. Before leaving, I turned to him sitting at the table. "Thanks again."

"You're welcome, brat."

I went to the car where Steph was waiting.

"Everything alright?" she asked, backing out of the driveway.

"Yep." My feelings were hurt, but I buried it deep. I was silent. So was Steph. I spent the rest of the ride listening to the radio and looking out the window. It reminded me a lot of Mama. Truth was me and Steph hadn't spoken much about what happened in Mississippi. Every time I tried to bring it up, she ignored me or changed the subject.

I'm sure they never called the police on Twin. He basically got away with raping me. For that reason, I couldn't forgive Steph. In my eyes, she was just as guilty as he was. I think ignoring what happened helped her deal with turmoil that was going on in her life. Maybe she felt if she didn't push the subject, Carlos would stay with her. Perhaps that's why she treated me and Meechie like we were her friends, not two wounded little girls she was responsible for taking care of.

Steph enrolled us at Mount Tahoma High School. Unlike at King, me and Meechie made a lot of friends. Steph let the boys from school come over and hang out with us. I thought it was weird. I think chilling with high school kids made her feel younger. I once heard a rumor at school that she was sleeping with one of our friends, Johnathon—a mixed boy with light eyes. I asked him, but he denied it. Still, I felt it was kind of gross for a 26-year-old woman to be screwing a 16-year-old boy. It gave me the same sick feeling in my stomach as the sight of Twin did.

Steph worked days as a nurse, but was usually home by 5:00 to cook dinner and get her kids ready for bed. Her and Carlos had an agreement. Every other week, they switched off with the kids. When they were spending the week with Carlos, Steph would have parties and make drinks for us and our friends.

"Did Steph tell you we're having a party tonight?" Meechie turned a page in her math book.

"Really?" I sighed. "It's Thursday."

"Yeah, that's what she said." She stretched her leg out from her crossed-legged position and wiggled her toes.

"Who's coming?"

"Probably Johnathon, the twins, and Shawn and Mike."

"No girls are coming?"

Meechie looked up from her math book. "Do girls ever come?"

I didn't like when Steph invited our friends over. I'm sure most teenage girls would love to have an alcoholic cousin who let boys come over and drink on a weekday, but I felt it was wrong.

"Dang! Why she always hanging with our friends?" I brushed my sandy brown hair into a ponytail and picked up some strands from my bed. Meechie shrugged her shoulders and went back to doing her homework.

There was a knock on the door. "Y'all ready to partay?" Steph did a little jig in the doorway.

"Yeah," we answered drily.

"Y'all don't act like it. Liven up. I'm going to make margaritas tonight. It's going to be fun! I'm 'bout to change out of my work clothes and get ready." Steph closed the door.

Me and Meechie looked at each other and shook our heads. A little while later, I could hear Steph singing to music in the living room.

"She's listening to Baby Got Back." I laughed.

I paused. "Meechie?"

"Yeah?"

"I don't want to be here anymore."

"What? Why?" She gave me her full attention.

I glanced at my orange toenail polish then answered. "I'd rather be with my dad."

"You would leave here to find a man you don't even know? You stupid."

"I know…but I bet he would believe me if I told him

someone raped me."

Meechie closed her book. "Here we go again. Steph told me you didn't even see who did that to you." She picked up her book and shoved it in her book bag. "I was right next to you and I didn't hear nothing. Why didn't you scream or something?"

I snapped back. "What was I going to do, Meechie? He covered my mouth."

"Shoot, you could've bit him or something." She plopped back on her bed.

"So, you don't believe me either?"

Meechie sat next to me. "All I'm saying is it's time to move past it. Have some fun for once in your life. All you do is frown and pout. Give Steph a chance. She'll make it up to you."

It was like I was listening to Grandma all over again. I couldn't believe what I was hearing. I didn't want to give Steph another chance. I didn't trust her. Also, I thought Meechie was the one who was stupid for believing in her. Furthermore, she never told me why she left me and Sissy in that wretched place, but took Meechie with her.

Around 7:00, Johnathon and the rest of the boys showed up.

"Come on, Meechie and Nikki," Steph called from the living room. "They're here!"

Steph greeted them with open arms and ushered them into the kitchen for their fill of alcoholic drinks.

I watched, but didn't partake. I didn't like the way I felt when I was drunk. Steph was always trying to get me to drink.

"You ain't drinking?" she asked.

I put my hand up. "Nah, I'm good. I don't like the way it makes me feel."

"Ahhh, come on. Stop being a party pooper. Just have a little bit." She handed me a cup.

I stared at the cup for a moment, until I started to feel the pain in my heart flare up once again. If this will take the pain away. I'll drink a little bit.

I grabbed the red plastic cup then drank the berry-tasting concoction to its end. Then I poured myself another cup and drank it quickly.

The room started to spin. I felt like I was on a merry-go-round—loud music and laughing faces passed me by. My stomach began to feel queasy, so I found my way to my room and lay on my bed. I closed my eyes for what seemed like a few minutes.

I was awakened by banging and yelling in the hallway. When I opened the door, I could see a crowd forming in the front of the house. I went on the front porch and saw Carlos and Steph fighting in the front yard. Instantly, I had a flashback of Mama and TeeTee fighting at Grandma's house.

Straight ahead there was a black Honda parked in the driveway with its lights on. There was so much chaos I could hardly decide if I should pay attention to the strange car or Carlos and Steph fighting.

"Go get that bitch, Meechie!" Steph yelled as her and Carolos tussled in the grass.

Meechie ran to the black car and banged on the window. A young Asian girl rolled down the window and barked some obscenities at Meechie. But, before she could roll up the window, Meechie reached in and pulled her out of the car by her long dark hair.

I gasped. "Oh my God, what in the hell is going on?"

Meechie kicked and punched the tiny Asian girl, but she managed to get away. She must have had enough of getting her butt kicked, because she jumped in her car and sped off. Carlos ran toward the car, but it was too late. She was gone.

"Ha-ha! That's what she gets!" Steph taunted Carlos. "That's what happens when you bring yo' hoes to my house."

"I didn't bring her over here—she followed me here!" he hollered. "What the hell is wrong with you?"

"Well, I can't put my hands on her, so I got my little cousin to beat that ass!"

Carlos slapped Steph, but she came back with a haymaker to his left jaw.

"Nigga, don't you ever put your hands on me again!" She kept on pounding on him until he tackled her.

They wrestled from the side of the yard to the sidewalk. She was kicking his ass so badly, he got frustrated and slammed her on the grass. I was frozen, but Meechie responded. "Uh-uh, you ain't goin' be hitting my cousin like that!" She came from behind Carlos and hit him in the head with a huge stick.

"Ouch!" He grabbed his head then turned to come after Meechie. Steph clocked him again, this time knocking him down.

A silver car quickly pulled up and stopped on a dime. Donny and his girlfriend Margie hopped out. His brown tailored suit moved sleekly with his medium-framed body. *Who called Donny?*

"Stephanie, cut it out!" he shouted.

"Daddy, he put his hands on me!" she explained.

It took Carlos a few moments to get up from the ground. "Mr. Avery, I can explain."

Donny stuck his hand out to stop Carlos and shook his head. "Son, you can't explain shit to me. The next time you put your hands on my daughter, I'm going to kill your ass!" Donny pulled back his suit jacket and revealed the shiny silver gun hidden in his waistband. "Do you understand?"

"Yes, sir." Carlos held up his hands and backed away.

"Now, get your ass out of here!" Donny raised his arm and pointed to the street.

Carlos didn't waste any time abiding by Donny's orders. He ran to his car and sped off. Donny calmed down the situation and sent everyone home before leaving himself.

Damn! How is being here any different from St. Louis? I could've stayed home if I would've known it was going to be like this!

Me and Meechie got ready for bed and talked a little about the foolishness that had occurred that night.

"Man, did you see how Steph was kicking Carlos's butt? She needs to be a boxer," I said, laughing. "Who was the girl in the car?"

"The girl Carlos is cheating on Steph with. I guess she followed him over here when he came to get some clothes for the kids."

"Why were they fighting anyway?" I pulled the

covers over my body and fluffed my pillow.

"He was mad because she was drinking with Johnathon and them."

I could see why he would be mad.

For a moment, Meechie was quiet. "You still want to leave?"

"Yeah, Steph got too much drama. I want to go to California."

Meechie let out a big sigh and turned over.

"Good night, little girl."

"Good night, Meechie."

* * *

Dear God,

I can't stay here anymore. I don't fit in. I want to see my daddy. I'm tired of fighting. I want to feel whole. If you won't help me find my daddy, please take me away in my sleep. I can't bear another day of this mess. Send someone to save me. I'm begging you. Anywhere is better than here. Love, Nikki.

CHAPTER

Twenty-One

MORNING CAME FAST. I dragged through the school day. My head was pounding from the drinks I had the night before. I barely made it. I couldn't wait to go home. When I made it to the house, I saw that Steph left me a note on the kitchen counter by the phone.

"Nikki, your Mama called. She wants you to call her back. 310-555-1212."

I got nervous. *Why does she want me to call her? Is Grandma okay?* I glanced at the note and threw it on the counter and walked away.

"Why is she calling me?" I asked myself again. I haven't spoken to her since I left St. Louis. *What does she want now?* I wanted to ignore the fact that she called, but I couldn't. A part of me missed Mama. I didn't feel like I belonged in Washington. At least, she was familiar—dysfunction and all.

I walked past the note a few times more before picking up the paper again. *Three-one-zero? Where is that?*

My curiosity had gotten the best of me. I dialed the number, hoping that she wouldn't answer.

"Hello?" Her voice hadn't changed.

"Hello? Mama?"

"Nikki?" Her voice got livelier.

"Yes."

"Oh, baby. Thank you for calling me." She sounded desperate. "How are you doing?"

"I'm good."

"I miss you so much."

I didn't return the sentiment. "Mama, where are you at?"

"I'm in California with my aunt Esther."

"Hi, baby." I heard a voice in the background.

My heart skipped a beat. "California? Why are you there?"

"For a new start, sweetheart." She paused. "Listen, baby, I was thinking you could come here and live with me."

I was silent as I thought about all the times she left me alone in that apartment without food, or anything else for that matter.

"I don't know, Mama."

"I know you're scared, but I promise things will be better. I stopped drinking and I'm going to church."

She stopped drinking? Maybe Mama has changed? She was right—I was scared. I wanted to believe her, but I was fearful that she would go back to her old ways.

"Mama, I have to think about it."

She stuttered. "Oh, okay. I...I understand. But, hey.

If you change your mind, let me know and I'll send you a ticket."

"Okay. I'll let you know."

"I love you, Nikki. Please give me a chance. I promise things will be better."

"I love you, too." I hung up the phone, reached in my bag and pulled out the piece of paper with my daddy's number on it. "Should I go, Daddy?"

"Go where?" I turned to find Steph standing behind me.

"I talked to my mama. She wants me to move to California with her."

"What?" She put her keys on the counter and dropped her work bag onto the floor. "You can't be thinking about going to live with her after all she put you through."

"I don't know, Steph. She said she stopped drinking."

"Ugh, Nikki. When are you going to learn? I know you love her, but she hasn't changed."

"You don't know that." I defended Mama.

"She probably just needs to get a check from the state or some food stamps or something. That's why she needs you to go there. Name one reason why you want to go to her, Nikki."

"I miss her, Steph. I know she's got problems, but she is my mama."

"Wake up, Nikki. She's going to get you way out in California, where you don't know anybody. At least when you were in St. Louis you had Aunt Rose and Meechie. What are you going to do when she starts flipping out on you?"

I paused. Steph was right. There was a possibility that my mama would trip out on me. I was afraid, but I missed her. I felt there was a chance that she could be normal. That her and I would finally have a relationship. No matter where I went, no one could fill the void that Mama left in my heart. I loved her. I wanted to be with her, in spite of how horrible she treated me.

I spoke up. "I'll find my daddy and live with him."

"Oh, Nikki." She paced the floor, then came and put her arms around me. "You know how this is going to turn out. Is this because of what happened in Mississippi?"

Tears started to swell in my eyes, so I looked away.

"Look at me, Nikki." She pulled my chin towards her. My nostrils flared and tears rolled down my face.

"I'm sorry that I didn't believe you, Nikki. I'm not perfect. I'm human too. You may not like everything I do, but at least you're cared for here." Steph looked at me with tears in her eyes, "Please don't go, Nikki. You will be making the worst mistake in your life."

In that moment, I felt Steph was sincere. I believed her. But, my whole being longed to be close to Mama. I felt there was something more waiting for me. I believed I had a chance of mending the broken parts within me.

"Steph, I can't stay. I'm sorry."

Steph broke down. "Please, Nikki."

"I have to see if she's changed. I just have to."

ABOUT THE AUTHOR

Christy Abram is an award-winning author and founder of Brown Girls Write—a self-care initiative aimed at helping women of color reflect, heal, and thrive through expressive writing. Christy lives in Seattle with her husband, two daughters and adorable grandson Chance. Learn more about Christy's work by visiting www.browngirlswrite.org

Made in the USA
San Bernardino, CA
12 August 2018